Teacher Guide

Physical Science

Passwords
Science Vocabulary

Developers: Joan Krensky and Maureen Devine Sotoohi

Cover Design: Susan Hawk

Photo Credits: Front cover: © Getty Images

Product Development and Design: Chameleon Publishing Services
Written by Barbara Klemetti Mindell

Reviewers: Curriculum Associates, LLC would like to acknowledge the contribution of the educators who reviewed *Passwords: Science Vocabulary* at various stages of its development. Their insightful comments have made our program a better one for teachers and students.

Gracie Alvear
Bilingual/ESL/Immigrant Student Service
Elementary Supervisor
Edinburg CISD
Edinburg, Texas

Rebecca Braaten
Secondary Science Senior Coordinator
Instructional Services Division
Polk County Schools
Bartow, Florida

Jackie Baldwin
Secondary Reading Senior Coordinator
Instructional Services Division
Polk County Schools
Bartow, Florida

Lorraine Cruz
Principal
Ames Middle School
Chicago, Illinois

Leonila Izaguirre
Bilingual-ESL Director
Pharr-San Juan-Alamo ISD
Pharr, Texas

Judy Lewis
Director, State and Federal Programs
Folsom Cordova Unified School District
Folsom, California

Dominique Mongeau
Categorical Program Adviser
Carson Street Elementary School
Los Angeles Unified School District
Carson, California

Connie Shaffer
Instructional Development Services
Orange County Public Schools
Orlando, Florida

Science Content Reviewer
Jennifer Murphy
Science Teacher
West Hartford Public Schools
West Hartford, Connecticut

Curriculum Associates

Table of Contents

ISBN 978-0-7609-4307-6
©2007—Curriculum Associates, LLC
North Billerica, MA 01862
Permission is granted for reproduction of the reproducible pages
in limited quantity for classroom use.
All Rights Reserved. Printed in USA.
15 14 13 12 11 10 9 8 7 6 5

Passwords: Science Vocabulary is designed to build the vocabulary essential to understanding the key concepts students are studying in science. The topic areas and vocabulary words used in *Passwords: Science Vocabulary* have been chosen based on the National Science Education Standards and the science standards developed by individual states. The topics and vocabulary words also align with the basal science textbooks of major publishers.

The *Passwords: Science Vocabulary* program consists of eight books, Levels A through H, as well as individual **Earth Science, Life Science,** and **Physical Science** books designed for use by older students.

Passwords: Science Vocabulary is recommended for all students who need practice with the vocabulary that will help them succeed in science. These students may include English language learners as well as other striving learners. See pages 9–11 of this teacher guide for vocabulary teaching strategies that will help teachers meet the needs of all their students.

While the lessons in *Passwords: Science Vocabulary* are grouped by topic area, each lesson may be taught independently. For a broad introduction to science, teachers may go through the book lesson by lesson. Alternatively, teachers may use only the lessons related to the science topic being taught in class. By providing an overview of grade-appropriate science topics, *Passwords: Science Vocabulary* may also be used to help students prepare and review for standardized tests in science.

The *Passwords: Science Vocabulary* student book reading selections are available on an audio CD. The CD is a useful tool to use with English language learners or other students who would benefit from listening to the reading selections multiple times. Auditory learners will find listening to the selections on the CD especially helpful.

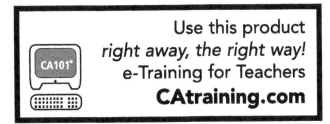

Use this product *right away, the right way!* e-Training for Teachers **CAtraining.com**

Passwords: Science Vocabulary student books have been written and designed to provide students with a text that is "considerate," or reader friendly. Three hallmarks of considerate text are: clear text structure, coherent writing, and audience appropriateness. **Passwords: Science Vocabulary** incorporates these characteristics of considerate text into every lesson.

Text Structure

The reading selections in **Passwords: Science Vocabulary** feature text structures that exhibit clear organizational patterns. In descriptive text, information is given in a logical order of importance. For sequential text, events are presented in the order in which they occur. In cause-and-effect text, the relation between the actions or events is clearly stated.

Coherent Writing

The science concepts and ideas presented in **Passwords: Science Vocabulary** are clearly stated. An introductory paragraph states the topic of the lesson. All the information in the reading selection connects to the topic. No extraneous material confuses readers. Headings and subheads highlight the cohesion of each text segment. Transitional words and phrases signal the relation between actions or concepts.

Audience Appropriateness

Although the readability of **Passwords: Science Vocabulary** reading selections is below grade level, the concepts and material in the passages are grade appropriate. Prereading activities activate students' prior knowledge. Activities that follow the reading selection help teachers evaluate student understanding.

Look for these signs of considerate text in the **Passwords: Science Vocabulary** student books.

- Short line length for increased readability
- Simple sentence structure
- Paragraphs with clear topic sentences and relevant supporting details
- Introductory subheads
- Target vocabulary words boldfaced in text
- Definitions of target vocabulary words near the first use of the word
- Simple font
- Clean page layout
- Appropriate, not overwhelming, visuals
- Illustrations support content

Each student book for Earth Science, Life Science, and Physical Science has 15 lessons. Each lesson introduces and practices ten key vocabulary words related to a single science topic.

Features of the Lesson

Each lesson of the student book contains these features:

- Target Vocabulary
- Lesson Opener
- Reading Selection
- Graphics
- Activities A–D
- Word Root
- Write!

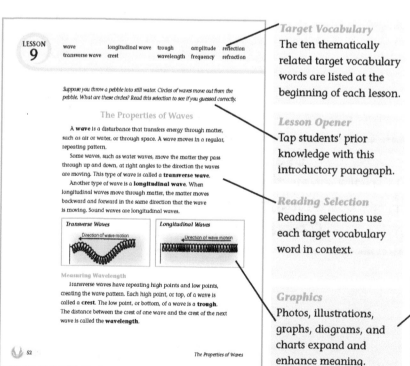

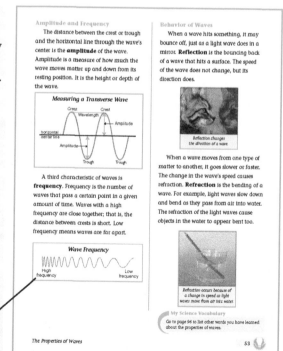

Target Vocabulary
The ten thematically related target vocabulary words are listed at the beginning of each lesson.

Lesson Opener
Tap students' prior knowledge with this introductory paragraph.

Reading Selection
Reading selections use each target vocabulary word in context.

Graphics
Photos, illustrations, graphs, diagrams, and charts expand and enhance meaning.

Progressively difficult activities follow each reading selection.

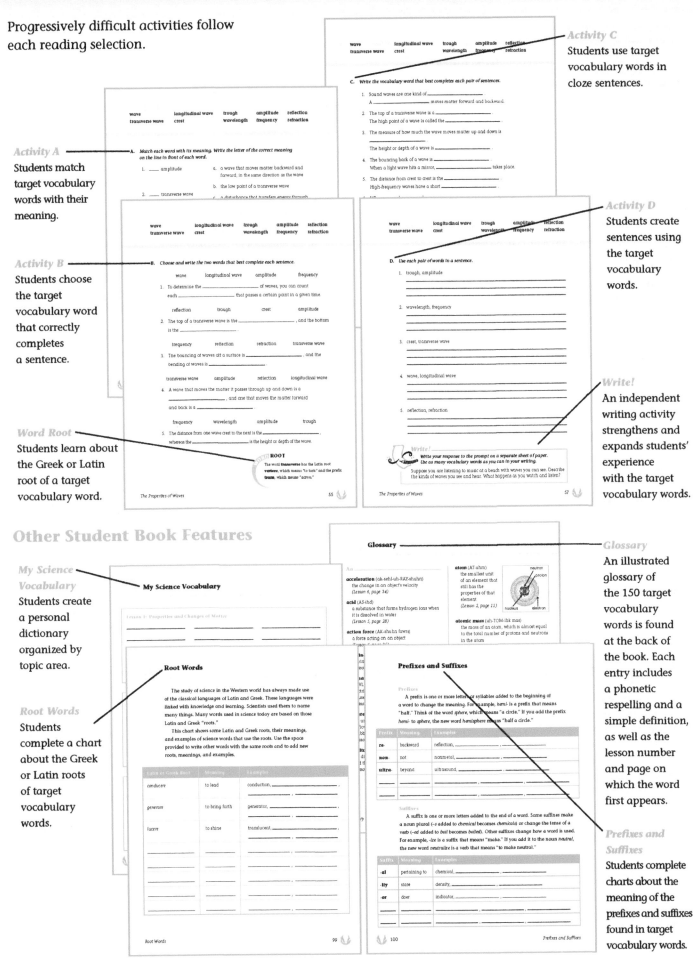

Activity A
Students match target vocabulary words with their meaning.

Activity B
Students choose the target vocabulary word that correctly completes a sentence.

Word Root
Students learn about the Greek or Latin root of a target vocabulary word.

Activity C
Students use target vocabulary words in cloze sentences.

Activity D
Students create sentences using the target vocabulary words.

Write!
An independent writing activity strengthens and expands students' experience with the target vocabulary words.

Other Student Book Features

My Science Vocabulary
Students create a personal dictionary organized by topic area.

Root Words
Students complete a chart about the Greek or Latin roots of target vocabulary words.

Glossary
An illustrated glossary of the 150 target vocabulary words is found at the back of the book. Each entry includes a phonetic respelling and a simple definition, as well as the lesson number and page on which the word first appears.

Prefixes and Suffixes
Students complete charts about the meaning of the prefixes and suffixes found in target vocabulary words.

Teacher Guide

The Teacher Guide for **Passwords: Science Vocabulary** contains resources that may be used to introduce, support, and extend students' science vocabulary studies. The Teacher Guide includes guided instruction for each student-book lesson.

Multi-Step Lesson Plan

Passwords: Science Vocabulary is built upon the premise that students benefit most from the direct instruction of vocabulary. Each lesson as presented in the Teacher Guide follows a multi-step lesson plan.

1. Introduction of the target vocabulary
2. Activation of students' prior knowledge
3. Provision of the meaning of unknown words
4. Creation by students of visual representations using graphic organizers
5. Further experiences with the target vocabulary
6. Activities that help students retain the word and its meaning

Listening, Speaking, Reading, and Writing

Passwords: Science Vocabulary provides opportunities for students to practice the target vocabulary words while listening, speaking, reading, and writing. These icons indicate opportunities for students to use the vocabulary words in different domains.

 Listening

 Speaking

 Reading

 Writing

Features of the Guided Teaching Lessons

Each lesson of the Teacher Guide contains these features:

- Target Vocabulary with definitions
- Cognates
- Vocabulary Strategy
- Lesson Summary
- Before Reading
- Word and Definition Cards
- Reproduced student book pages
- During Reading
- After Reading
- Annotated student book activity pages
- Extensions
- Ideas for introducing the Write! activity
- Sample answer for Write!
- Word Root extension

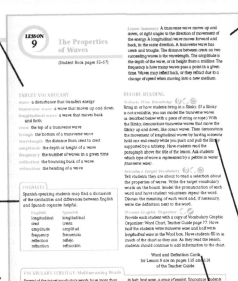

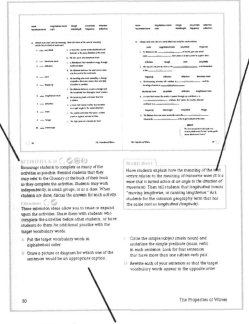
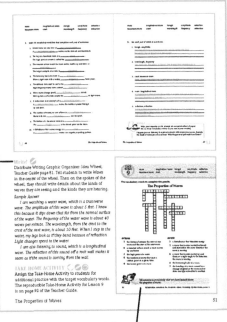

Other Teacher Guide Features

- **Vocabulary Teaching Strategies**
Information and tips about how to employ vocabulary teaching strategies that have proven effective with struggling learners and English language learners begin on page 9.

- **Research Summary**
A summary of the research that forms the basis of *Passwords: Science Vocabulary* is on pages 12–15.

- **Reproducibles**
Pages 76–128 of the Teacher Guide contain reproducibles for you to share with students.

  ### Graphic Organizers
  You may either photocopy the graphic organizers for students to use or use the sample graphic organizer as a model for students to create their own. The Before Reading section of each guided lesson suggests a particular vocabulary graphic organizer to use with the lesson. The Write! section of each guided lesson suggests a writing graphic organizer to use with the Write! activity.

  - **Vocabulary Graphic Organizers**

    Word Web   Students write a topic in the central circle. Then they group related target vocabulary words in the outer circles. Beside each circle, they write a phrase that explains why they grouped the words together.

    Word Chart   Students use this graphic organizer to write a target vocabulary word, record its definition, list examples, use the word in a sentence, and draw a picture, a diagram, or write an equation about the word.

    Four Square   In this graphic organizer, students write a target vocabulary word in the center rectangle. They illustrate the word, use the word in a sentence, write a definition of the word, and list the part of the word (roots, prefixes, and suffixes) in the surrounding squares.

    Word Arrow   Students use this graphic organizer to record target vocabulary words that follow a progression or sequence. They write the words that begin the sequence on the left of the arrow and add the target vocabulary words in the appropriate order, proceeding right to the arrow point.

  - **Writing Graphic Organizers**

    Main Idea and Details Chart   This graphic organizer may be used with a variety of writing assignments. Students write a main idea in one box and the details that support it in another box.

    Idea Wheel   This variation of a web can be used with different types of writing. Students write a topic or main idea in the center of the wheel. On the spokes of the wheel, they add details or ideas about the topic or main idea.

    Narrative Map   Use this graphic organizer when students are asked to write a narrative. They record the character(s) and setting(s) in the top boxes and the events of the narrative in the bottom box.

    Sequence Chart   A sequence chart provides students with a visual representation of the steps in a process. In this organizer, they record the steps, in order, in a series of boxes.

  ### Word and Definition Cards
  Word cards for each target vocabulary word as well as cards with the definitions for the words are on pages 99–128 of this Teacher Guide. You may either cut the cards out of the book or photocopy them, cut them apart, and then use them. For ideas on how to use the word and definition cards, see page 10 of this Teacher Guide.

  ### Take-Home Activities
  Each student book lesson has a take-home activity for additional practice and an opportunity for students to share what they have learned with family members.

Vocabulary Teaching Strategies

These teaching strategies have been shown to be effective with English language learners, but all students who are studying vocabulary will find them helpful.

Accessing Prior Knowledge

Like their English-speaking peers, English language learners come to the classroom with a large body of knowledge. The challenge as a teacher of English language learners is tapping into this knowledge. Before introducing a lesson topic, ask students what they already know about the subject. By doing this, you not only acknowledge students' experiences, but you also find out what information and misinformation students have about the topic. This will enable you to plan a more relevant and focused lesson. Each student book lesson of **Passwords: Science Vocabulary** begins with an introductory paragraph written to tap into students' prior knowledge and to provide motivation for reading. In addition, this Teacher Guide includes a prior knowledge activity for each lesson.

Picture File

Use magazines or Web sources to create a file of pictures for each science topic. Students will enjoy looking for pictures and pasting them to construction paper. Use the pictures to illustrate target vocabulary words or key concepts. Pictures can be used before, during, or after reading in matching games, gallery walks, and as writing prompts.

Graphic Organizers

This Teacher Guide includes four vocabulary graphic organizers and four writing graphic organizers that can be reproduced for use by students. (See pages 76–83.)

Vocabulary graphic organizers can provide students with a visual representation of a word's meaning by showing examples, synonyms, drawings, descriptions, or the definition of the word. Students can add to the graphic organizer as their understanding of the word increases.

Writing graphic organizers help students organize their thoughts and plan their writing. The writing graphic organizers included in this Teacher Guide are intended for use with different kinds of Write! activities.

Total Physical Response

Total Physical Response, or TPR, is a language-teaching method first developed by Dr. James Asher, a professor of psychology. Asher based his method on his observations of how children learn their native language. In TPR, teachers replace parents, modeling verbal commands, while students respond physically. As a language-teaching method, TPR emphasizes listening and physical response over written language. It has been found to be an effective method for teaching vocabulary. In using TPR to teach vocabulary, teachers and students use movement to associate a word with its meaning. For example, to teach the target vocabulary word *rotate*, have your students get up and turn around. To teach the word *orbit*, have students walk around an object placed in the center of the classroom. To use TPR in your classroom, give commands that require a physical response from students. When they are ready, students can reverse roles, giving commands to you and to fellow students.

Context Clues

Students need to be directly instructed on how to use context clues to help them figure out the meaning of unknown words. There are several different kinds of context clues.

- **Definition**
  In this type of context clue, a definition, or restatement, of the unknown word is provided in the text. Words that signal a definition context clue include *means, refers to,* or *is.* Definition context clues are frequently used in **Passwords: Science Vocabulary**.

- **Synonym**
  Writers sometimes use familiar words with similar meanings to build meaning for an unknown or unfamiliar word.

- **Example**
  Point out to students that writers will sometimes provide an example that will help them figure out the meaning of an unfamiliar word. Words that may signal an example include *like, these, for example,* and *such as.*

Cognates

Cognates are words in different languages that resemble one another in both sound and meaning. Spanish and English have many cognates, especially in the area of science where words in both languages draw upon Latin and Greek roots. Some cognates are spelled identically, although pronunciation differs; for example the words *capital, tractor,* and *radio.* Others are spelled similarly; *rayo* and *ray.* Other words that seem similar are not cognates at all. *Bigote* does not mean "bigot"; it means "mustache."

Teachers cannot assume that Spanish-speaking students will automatically or correctly connect an English word with a Spanish cognate. To help students develop the ability to recognize cognates, each **Passwords: Science Vocabulary** Teacher Guide lesson includes a list of the Spanish cognates for the target vocabulary in that lesson. As you discuss these cognates with students, point out spelling patterns, such as *-tion* (English) and *-ción* (Spanish). This will help students develop generalizations about language patterns and enhance their ability to use their knowledge of their native language to learn English. Encourage your Spanish-speaking students to guess at the meaning of words in English based on their knowledge of Spanish. If you read the selections aloud, ask Spanish speakers to indicate when they think they hear a cognate. If students read the selections themselves, have them write down the words they think might be cognates. Discuss possible cognates when students have finished reading the selection. Write the word pairs on the board and have students come to the board and circle the similarities between the two words. Have students look for patterns. Students who speak languages other than Spanish may also be able to find English cognates of words from their native languages.

Greek and Latin Roots

Introducing the study of Greek and Latin roots to students who are learning English may initially seem to be adding another layer of difficulty to language learning. However, students who speak a romance language (Spanish, French, Italian, Portuguese, Romanian) will often find that the Latin or Greek root of an English word is similar to a word they know in their own language. Students who speak Haitian Creole may find that their native language, which draws heavily upon French, also has many links to Latin.

When teaching students how to use roots to determine word meaning, remind them that many long English words are made up of smaller parts. The root of the word is the part that contains the most important aspect of the word's meaning. For example, if students come across the word *astronomy* and they recognize the root *astro* from their study of Greek and Latin roots and they remember that the root *astro* is related to star, they can begin to figure out that *astronomy* has something to do with stars.

Students will find a chart of Greek and Latin roots, with examples of target vocabulary words that have those roots, on page 99 of the student book.

Prefixes and Suffixes

A prefix is a word part that is attached to the beginning of a base word. A suffix is a word part that is attached to the end of a base word. The meaning of a prefix or suffix combines with the meaning of the base word. For example, the prefix *tri-,* meaning "three," combines with *angle* to form *triangle,* a figure with three angles. The suffix *-ward,* meaning "in the direction of," combines with *back* to form *backward.* Knowing the meaning of common prefixes and suffixes is another tool students can use to help them figure out the meaning of unknown words and remember the meaning of words they are learning.

Students will find a chart of common prefixes and suffixes, with examples of target vocabulary words that have these prefixes or suffixes, on page 100 of the student book.

Word Cards

This Teacher Guide includes reproducible word and definition cards on pages 99–128. Each page contains one lesson's words or definitions. These cards can be used in teacher-led activities, and small group activities, to introduce new vocabulary, and to review vocabulary and concepts. Word cards are helpful to visual, kinesthetic, and aural learners. Word cards provide students with visual cues and constant reinforcement. Many word card activities require you to create copies of the cards. You can photocopy the cards on cardstock or on plain paper. If you want to use the cards as flashcards, with the definition on the back, photocopy the pages as two-sided copies. For many activities, however, you will need cards with one blank side and the word or the definition on the other side. After you make the copies, cut the cards apart. Store the cards in labeled plastic zipper bags for easy access. You might want to provide each student with a set of cards, you might consider having students create their own cards using blank 3½" × 5" file cards. Although you will certainly come up with many ideas of how to use these cards on your own, here are a few activities to begin with.

- **Word Wall**

  A Word Wall can be a great tool in helping students learn vocabulary. Although words are generally displayed on a bulletin board, you can also use more portable display surfaces, such as a shower curtain or a trifold board. Add words to the Word Wall as you introduce the target vocabulary. Review the words daily. Change the words as you begin a new lesson. Word Walls lend themselves to a variety of activities.

  ### Five Clues

  Have each student number their paper from one to five. Give a clue about one of the words on the Word Wall. Students should write down the word they think you are thinking of. Keep giving clues (up to five) until everyone has guessed the word you were thinking of.

  ### Lights On!

  You'll need a flashlight for this activity. Turn off the classroom lights. Then point the flashlight at one word on the Word Wall. Call on a student to read the word and either use it in a sentence or provide the definition. When the student is successful, it is his or her turn to point the flashlight at a word and choose another student to read the word.

  ### Wordo

  Provide each student with a bingo-type grid with six blank spaces. Tell students to fill in the blanks with words from the Word Wall. Put the corresponding definition cards into a jar. Pull the definition cards from the jar one by one. Read the definition and have students cover the corresponding word on their grid with a marker. When the entire card is covered, Wordo!

- **Card Games**

  The word cards can be used in many different card games, some of which are variations of games played with regular playing cards. Here are a few ideas for games using the word cards.

  ### Concentration

  The object of this game is to find matching pairs. Prepare two sets of cards. One set of cards has the target vocabulary words and the other set has the definitions. Prepare from 10 cards (for 5 matches) to 30 cards (15 matches). Mix up the two sets of cards. Place the cards face down in rows. Players take turns turning over pairs of cards. If the cards match, the player makes a sentence using the vocabulary word. If the cards don't match, play goes to the next player. If the student successfully creates a sentence using the vocabulary word, he or she goes again. The player with the most cards at the end is the winner.

  ### Guess the Word

  This game is for four students, playing in pairs. Prepare a card for each target vocabulary word. Put the cards face down in the middle of the table. The first student of the first pair picks a card and gives a one-word clue to his or her partner that will enable the partner to guess the vocabulary word. If the partner does not guess the word, the word goes to a member of the other pair who gives a hint to his or her partner. The team that successfully guesses the word keeps the card. The team with the most cards wins.

What Is the Need for *Passwords: Science Vocabulary?*

The curriculum area of science has been receiving increased attention at both the federal and state levels. Several initiatives have focused the educational spotlight onto science education, resulting in increased demand for improved instruction and student achievement. Some active programs and initiatives that are creating a need for academic science vocabulary instruction are:

- The NCLB Act of 2001 requires states to assess students' progress in science at least once in each of these three grade spans (3–5, 6–9, 10–12) each year, starting in 2007.

- "English language learners (ELLs) who experience slow vocabulary development are less able to comprehend text at grade level than their English-only peers. Such students are likely to perform poorly on assessments in these areas and are at risk of being diagnosed as learning disabled" (August, Carlo, Dressler, & Snow, 2005).

- American Competitiveness Initiative—In 2006, President Bush's education agenda is concentrating on strengthening America's educational system in the areas of STEM (science, technology, engineering, and mathematics). This initiative is currently affecting high school curriculum. However, schools may start preparing for this initiative in elementary and middle school.

The educational spotlight will continue to focus on math and science education as accountability deadlines approach and as initiatives are finalized. ***Passwords: Science Vocabulary*** unites students with a singular goal of successfully learning the academic language of science. This goal is attainable through the instructional features and strategies that research has proven to be effective with diverse student populations.

Why Is *Passwords: Science Vocabulary* Helpful to ELL Students?

Academic Language Proficiency is the ability of the student to comprehend, speak, read, and write when the context is reduced and the topic is cognitively demanding. Examples of cognitively demanding activities are reading textbooks, writing long compositions, learning new concepts, and mastering local and state requirements that test students on the academic language of each content area. Zelasko & Antunez (2000) state that "without mastery of classroom English, they [ELL students] will have difficulty competing academically in an all-English setting." The importance of learning academic language is confirmed by additional researchers:

- "Vocabulary development is one of the greatest challenges to reading instruction for ELLs, because in order to read fluently and comprehend what is written, students need to use not just phonics, but context" (Antunez, 2002).

- "For English language learners, academic English is like a third language, their second language being the social English of the hallways, community, and media. And whereas students are exposed to social English in various settings, academic language acquisition is generally limited to the classroom. . . . Many English language learners, even those with well-developed social language, struggle to master the complex language of school" (Zwiers, 2004/2005).

What Are the Strategies and Features in *Passwords: Science Vocabulary* that Research Has Proven to Be Effective with ELL Students?

Science is a cognitively demanding school subject. The first step to comprehending the content of a school subject is to understand the vocabulary and language of the school subject. ***Passwords: Science Vocabulary*** incorporates ELL instructional recommendations from content-area experts for teaching vocabulary.

Marzano & Pickering (2005), in *Building Academic Vocabulary*, promotes a six-step process for teaching new terms. This process is also integrated in ***Passwords: Science Vocabulary***.

Step 1: Provide a description, an explanation, or an example of the new term (along with a nonlinguistic representation).

Step 2: Ask students to restate the description, explanation, or example in their own words.

Step 3: Ask students to construct a picture, symbol, or graphic representing the term or phrase.

Step 4: Engage students periodically in activities that help them add to their knowledge of the terms.

Step 5: Engage students periodically to discuss the terms with one another.

Step 6: Involve students periodically in games that allow them to play with terms.

Additionally, educational experts and researchers from numerous professional organizations (National Science Teachers Association, English Language Summit), have created a list of instructional recommendations that have been found to be effective, especially with ELL students. While these organizations are separate entities, they share some common recommendations. These recommendations are integrated throughout **Passwords: Science Vocabulary**.

Passwords: Science Vocabulary Uses . . .	**Research Says . . .**
Direct Instruction within Context (SB, Reading Passage & Activities A–D)	*"The teaching of individual words is most effective when learners are given both definitional and contextual information, when learners actively process the new word meanings, and when they experience multiple encounters with words"* (Graves & Watts-Taffe, 2002). *"It is important to teach vocabulary within the scientific context, not in isolation"* (NSTA, 2006).
Prior-knowledge Activation (SB, Prereading Activity; TG)	*"Students who lack in academic background knowledge also lack in academic achievement. To be most effective, a teacher should be aware of each student's level of background knowledge"* (Marzano & Pickering, 2005). *"To facilitate communication of content knowledge, teachers can offer support in several ways: Plan adequate time to activate students' prior knowledge and encourage students to share what they already know in journals, small groups, or paired brainstorming sessions"* (Rolón, 2002/2003).
Collaborative Learning (SB, Prereading Activity & Activities A–D; TG)	*"Students interacting verbally with other native speakers of English pick up vocabulary and content knowledge"* (English Language Summit, 2004). *"Research and common sense . . . confirm that interacting with other people about what we are learning deepens the understanding of everyone involved—particularly when we are learning new terms"* (Marzano & Pickering, 2005).
Differentiated Instruction (SB, Activities A–D; TG)	*"Because children differ, no single text nor any single task can be appropriate for all children in a classroom . . ."* (Allington, 2005). *"Numerous theorists and contemporary translators of brain research propose that students do not learn effectively when tasks are too simple or too complex for their particular readiness levels. Rather, say these researchers, tasks must be moderately challenging for the individual for growth to occur"* (Tomlinson, 2004).
Parental Engagement (TG, Take-Home Activities)	*"The evidence is consistent, positive, and convincing: families have a major influence on their children's achievement in school and through life"* (National Center for Family & Community Connections with Schools, 2002).
Total Physical Response (TG, Vocabulary Teaching Strategies section, During Reading Activity)	*"Having children physically act out songs, poems, or readings—all forms of TPR methodology—is an effective way to support vocabulary development"* (Drucker, 2003). *In a research synthesis, Slavin & Cheung (2005) state that teachers of English language learners may use language development strategies, such as total physical response, to help students internalize new vocabulary.*
Considerate Text (SB, Reading Passages)	*"Certain features of text make it more 'considerate,' or easier to read and understand. The features should have clear concepts, consistent text structure, references that are easy to locate, and vocabulary that is precise and relates clearly to the subject. . . . A considerate text makes comprehension easier"* (Dyck & Pemberton, 2002).

(Continues)

Passwords: Science Vocabulary Uses . . .	**Research Says . . .**
Graphic Organizers (Semantic Feature Analysis & Semantic Mapping) (TG, Pre- & Post-reading Activities)	*Hedrick, Harmon, & Linerode (2004, 2000) have analyzed content-area textbooks and have concluded that "textbooks infrequently include visual representations of concepts as a vocabulary instructional strategy."* *"Students with very limited English proficiency show their understanding in a variety of ways. ELL students can demonstrate their knowledge through visual representations" (Crowther, 2006).*
Clear and Explicit Illustrations and Artwork (SB, Reading Passages)	*"Giving an ESL student a nonlinguistic representation will provide a way for them to understand the meaning of the term that is not dependent on an understanding of English" (Marzano & Pickering, 2005).* *"Pictures and other graphic aids provide additional sources of meaning other than the definition of a word" (NSTA, 2006).*
Deep Word Study Activities (Roots, Prefixes, Suffixes, Cognates) (SB/TG)	*Students may find learning English easier if there are similar roots and pre/suffixes between their first language and English. Hansen (2006) suggests exploring cognates in order to aid students in making connections between their first language and English.* *"Teaching a word's facets of meaning moves students beyond a narrow definition of a word" (Beck, McKeown, Kucan, 2002).*
Word Play Activities (TG, Take-Home Activities, Word Cards)	*Researchers (Marzano & Pickering, 2005; NSTA, 2006; Paynter, Bodrova, & Doty, 2005) stress that word play builds strong connection to newly learned vocabulary.* *"Activities using words in games, connecting words, and manipulating words creatively result in excellent student learning" (Beck et al., 2002).*
Association/ Connection Methods: (Personal Connection, Picture Connection, Word Connection) (SB/TG, throughout each lesson, Glossary)	*"When teaching academic vocabulary, students should be active in developing their understanding of words and ways to learn them. This can include semantic mapping and word sorts, and illustrating vocabulary words" (NSTA, 2006).* *"This step is particularly important to ESL students. Whereas they might be constrained in their ability to devise a linguistic description, explanation, or example, they will not be constrained in their ability to create a nonlinguistic representation . . . These representations will most likely reflect the students' native culture, which is exactly the intent. Learning academic terms involves making connections with things familiar to us, and these things commonly arise from experiences native to our culture" (Marzano, 2005).*
Modeling Through Audio (*Passwords* Audio CD)	*"When English language learners can simultaneously hear and read content-related information . . . it helps them decipher the text structures commonly found in textbooks" (Rubinstein-Ávila, 2006).*
Read Alouds (TG)	*"Teacher read-alouds are perhaps the most consistent activity used by classroom teachers that provides frequent, if not daily, opportunities to enhance the literacy of ELLs by integrating effective vocabulary development practices" (Hickman, Pollard-Durodola, & Vaughn, 2004).*
Speaking, Listening, Reading, Writing Experiences (SB/TG, throughout each lesson)	*"Successful word learning is active. Students learn words by using them. Thinking, saying, and writing new words help us make new words our own" (Bromley, 2003).* *García (1999) recommended that teachers use ". . . curriculum materials that are rich in opportunities for speaking, listening, reading, and writing in English."*

References

Alber, S. R., & Foil, C. R. (2002). Fun and effective ways to build your students' vocabulary. *Intervention in School & Clinic, 37*.

Allington, R. L. (2005). The other five "pillars" of effective reading instruction. *Reading Today, 22*(6).

Anderson, T. H., & Armbruster, B. B. (1984). Studying. In P. D. Pearson, R. Barr, M. L. Kamil, & P. Mosenthal (Eds.), *Handbook of reading research* (Vol. 1, pp. 657–679). White Plains, NY: Longman.

Antunez, B. (2002). English language learners and the five essential components of reading comprehension. Accessed February 27, 2006 from http://www.readingrockets.org/articles/341#vocab.

Asher, J. (1969). The total physical response approach to second language learning. *Modern Language Journal, 53*, 3–18.

Association of American Publishers. (Fall 2004). English Language Learners summit proceedings, AAP School Division. Summit on English Language Learners. The Washington Court Hotel, Washington, DC. October 12, 2004. Accessed January 16, 2006 from http://www.publishers.org/SchoolDiv/research/research_03/research_03_Rep_05.htm.

August, D., Carlo, M., Dressler, C., & Snow, C. (2005). The critical role of vocabulary development for English language learners. *Learning Disabilities Research & Practice, 20*(1), 50–57.

Baumann, J. F., Kame'enui, E. J., & Ash, G. E. (2003). Research on vocabulary instruction: Voltaire redux. In J. Flood, D. Lapp, J. R. Squire, & J. M. Jensen (Eds.), *Handbook of research on the teaching of the English language arts* (2nd ed., pp. 752–785). Mahwah, NJ: Erlbaum.

Beck, I., & McKeown, M. (2001). Text talk: Capturing the benefits of read-aloud experiences for young children. *Reading Teacher, 55*(1), 10–20.

Beck, I. L., McKeown, M. G., & Kucan, L. (2002). *Bringing words to life: Robust vocabulary instruction*. New York: Guilford Press.

Bromley, K. (2003, April). Vocabulary S-t-r-e-t-c-h-e-r-s, *Instructor, 112*(7).

Crowther, D. T. (Ed.). (2006). *Science for English-language Learners: K–12 Classroom Strategies*. Arlington, VA: NSTA Press.

Dobb, F. (2004). *Essential elements of science instruction for English learners*, 2nd ed. Los Angeles, CA: California Science Project.

Drucker, M. J. (2003). What reading teachers should know about ESL learners: Good teaching is teaching for all. *The Reading Teacher, 57*(1).

Dyck, N., & Pemberton, J. B. (2002). A model for making decisions about text adaptations. *Intervention in School & Clinic, 38*(1).

Fathman, A. K., & Crowther, D. T. (Eds.). (2006). *Science for English language learners: K–12 classroom strategies*. Arlington, VA: NSTA Press.

García, E. (1999). *Student cultural diversity: Understanding and meeting the challenge* (2nd ed.). Boston: Houghton Mifflin.

Graves, M. F., & Watts-Taffe, S. M. (2002). The place of word consciousness in a research-based vocabulary program in *What Research has to say about reading instruction*. Newark, DE: International Reading Association.

Hansen, L. (2006). Strategies for ELL success: Simple strategies to incorporate into inquiry science for English language learners. *Science and Children*, 23–25.

Hedrick, W. B., Harmon, J. M., & Linerode, P. M. (2004). Teachers' beliefs and practices of vocabulary instruction with social studies textbooks in Grades 4–8. *Reading Horizons, 45*(2), 103–125.

Hedrick, W. B., Harmon, J. M., & Linerode, P. M. (2000). Content analysis of vocabulary instruction in social studies textbooks for grades 4–8. *Elementary School Journal, 100*(3), 253–271.

Henderson, A. T., & Mapp, K. L. (2002). *A new wave of evidence: The impact of school, family, and community connections on student achievement. Annual Synthesis 2002.* National Center for Family & Community Connections with Schools. Austin: Southwest Educational Development Laboratory.

Hickman, P., Pollard-Durodola, S., & Vaughn, S. (2004). Storybook reading: Improving vocabulary and comprehension for English-language learners. *Reading Teacher, 57*(8), 720–730.

Jesness, J. (2004). *Teaching English language learners K–12: A quick-start guide for the new teacher*. Thousand Oaks, CA: Corwin Press.

Marzano, R. J., & Pickering, D. J. (2005). *Building Academic Vocabulary: Teacher's manual*. Alexandria, VA: ASCD.

McCarthey, S. J. (2000). Home-school connections: A review of the literature. *Journal of Educational Research, 93*(3), 145–154.

National Reading Panel. (2000). *Report of the national reading panel: Teaching children to read*. Washington, DC: National Institute of Child Health and Human Development.

National Research Council. (2006). Multiple origins, uncertain destinies: Hispanics and the American future. Panel on Hispanics in the United States. M. Tienda and F. Mitchell, eds. Committee on Population, Division of Behavioral and Social Sciences and Education. Washington, DC: The National Academies Press.

Paynter, D. E., Bodrova, E., & Doty, J. K. (2005). *For the love of words: Vocabulary instruction that works, grades K–6*. San Francisco: Jossey-Bass.

Richek, M. A. (2005, February). Words are wonderful: Interactive, time-efficient strategies to teach meaning vocabulary. *Reading Teacher, 58*(5), 414–423.

Rolón, C. A. (2002/2003). Educating Latino students. *Educational Leadership, 60*(4), 40–3.

Rubinstein-Ávila, E. (2006). Connecting With Latino Learners. *Educational Leadership, 63*(5), 38–43.

Slavin, R. E., & Cheung, A. (2005). Synthesis of research on language of reading instruction for English language learners. *Review of Educational Research Summer, 75*(2), 247–284.

Spellings, M. (2006). Secretary Spellings announces national math and science summit for girls and discusses American competitiveness. Accessed March 1, 2006 at http://www.ed.gov/news/pressreleases/2006/02/02282006.html.

Tomlinson, C. A. (2004, April). Differentiation in diverse settings. *School Administrator, 61*(7).

U. S. Department of Education. (2004). *Parental involvement: Title One, Part A Non-regulatory guidance*. Washington, DC: No Child Left Behind.

U. S. Department of Education. (2006). Strengthening Education: Meeting the Challenge of a Changing World. Accessed on February 15, 2006 at http://www.ed.gov/about/inits/ed/competitiveness/challenge.html.

Zelasko, N., & Antunez, B. (2000). *If your child learns in two languages: A parent's guide for improving educational opportunities for children acquiring English as a second language*. National Clearinghouse of Bilingual Education: The George Washington University: Graduate School of Education and Human Development. Washington, DC.

Zwiers, J. (2004/2005). The third language of academic English. *Educational Leadership, 62*(4), 60–63.

LESSON 1

Properties and Changes of Matter

(Student Book pages 4–9)

TARGET VOCABULARY

mass the amount of matter

volume the amount of space matter takes up

density how tightly packed matter is

buoyant force the upward push of a fluid

displacement the volume of fluid pushed aside by an object placed in the fluid

physical change a change in the size, shape, or state of matter

melting point the temperature at which a solid turns to a liquid

freezing point the temperature at which a liquid changes to a solid

boiling point the temperature at which a liquid changes to a gas

chemical change a change that creates one or more new substances

COGNATES

Spanish-speaking students may find a discussion of the similarities and differences between English and Spanish cognates helpful.

English	Spanish
mass	masa
volume	volumen
density	densidad
force	fuerza
displacement	desplazamiento
physical change	cambio físico
point	punto
chemical change	cambio químico

Lesson Summary Matter has mass and volume. The density of a type of matter is found by dividing the mass by the volume. Fluids exert a buoyant force. An object placed in a fluid displaces an amount of fluid equal to its volume. The object will sink if it is denser than the fluid, and float if it is less dense. A physical change in matter is a change in state. Changes of state occur when matter reaches its melting or freezing point, and its boiling point. A chemical change is one that creates products different from the raw materials.

BEFORE READING

Activate Prior Knowledge

Ask students to name and describe types of matter they can see in the classroom. List students' responses on the board. Then have students read the paragraph above the title of the lesson. Have them refer to the list on the board for examples of possible answers to the questions. As students read the lesson, have them add information to the list.

Introduce Target Vocabulary

Tell students they are about to read a selection about properties and changes of matter. Write the target vocabulary words on the board. Model the pronunciation of each word and have student volunteers repeat the word. Discuss the meaning of each word and, if necessary, write the definition next to the word.

Present Graphic Organizer

Provide each student with a copy of Vocabulary Graphic Organizer: Word Web, Teacher Guide page 76. Have students write *Matter* in the center circle of the web. As they read the lesson, have students group related target vocabulary words in the outer circles. Have them write a phrase next to each circle that explains why they grouped the words together. Tell them they may add circles, if necessary.

Word and Definition Cards
for Lesson 1 are on pages 99 and 100
of the Teacher Guide.

VOCABULARY STRATEGY: Textbook Features

Discuss with students how features in textbooks, such as headings and boldfaced words, tell readers what to pay attention to. Ask students what it usually means when a word is printed in bold in a textbook. *(The word is one that students need to know or to learn.)* Tell students that the meaning of a boldfaced word is often given in the sentence in which the word appears. Direct attention to the word *mass* and its definition in the first paragraph of the lesson. As students read the lesson, have them note each boldfaced word and circle the sentence with its definition.

Properties and Changes of Matter

LESSON 1

mass   density   displacement   melting point   boiling point
volume   buoyant force   physical change   freezing point   chemical change

Look at all the types of matter around you. What are some properties that make one type of matter different from another? How does matter change? Read this selection to learn more about matter.

Properties and Changes of Matter

Mass, Volume, and Density

All matter has mass and takes up space. **Mass** is the amount of matter. Mass is measured in grams and is often mistaken for weight. An object's weight, though, depends on the force of gravity acting on it. If an object is moved, its weight can change, but its mass stays the same.

The amount of space that matter takes up is its **volume**. The volume of a liquid is often measured in liters or milliliters. A regularly shaped solid is often measured in cubic centimeters. One milliliter equals one cubic centimeter.

Different types of matter have different densities. **Density** is the amount of matter packed into a certain volume. You can find the density of an object by dividing its mass by its volume.

This balance scale measures mass in grams.

This graduated beaker measures liquid volume in milliliters.

This solid has a mass of 9 grams and a volume of 3 cubic centimeters.
$$density = \frac{9\,g}{3\,cm^3} = \frac{3\,g}{cm^3}$$

Sinking and Floating

A fluid applies an upward force on objects called the **buoyant force**. The buoyant force pushes up on an object placed in the fluid and makes the object seem lighter.

An object placed in a fluid causes the fluid to rise. That happens because the object pushes aside a volume of fluid equal to the object's own volume. The volume of fluid pushed aside is the **displacement**. An object floats if its weight is equal to or less than the weight of its displacement. An object sinks if its weight is greater than the weight of its displacement.

Whether an object floats or sinks also depends on its density and the density of the fluid. If the density of an object is greater than the density of the fluid, the object will overcome the buoyant force acting on it and sink. If its density is less than or equal to the fluid's density, the object will float.

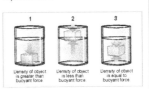
Density of object is greater than buoyant force. Density of object is less than buoyant force. Density of object is equal to buoyant force.

Physical and Chemical Changes

A **physical change** is a change in the size, shape, or state of matter, with no new matter being formed. Adding or taking heat away from a solid, liquid, or gas, for example, changes its state. The temperature at which a particular solid turns to a liquid is its **melting point**. The **freezing point** is the temperature at which the liquid changes to a solid. The melting and freezing points of one type of matter are the same. The temperature at which a liquid changes to a gas is its **boiling point**.

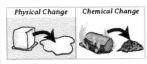
Physical Change   Chemical Change

A **chemical change** is a change in matter that creates one or more new substances. The particles that make up the matter break apart and regroup to form a different kind of matter. Energy is always gained or lost during a chemical change.

My Science Vocabulary
Go to page 94 to list other words you have learned about properties and changes of matter.

4   Properties and Changes of Matter

Properties and Changes of Matter   5

DURING READING

Read the selection aloud to students, stopping at the end of each paragraph or section. Review any words or concepts that students are having trouble with. Remind students that there is a glossary at the back of their book that contains all of the words that appear in boldfaced type in the lesson.

- Have students read each caption in the diagram on page 5. Explain that dense matter has molecules that are packed close together and that density is a characteristic of matter. A larger volume of the same matter has the same density as a smaller volume.

- Point out that physical changes are normally phase changes, or state changes. The temperatures at which these changes occur are characteristic of the type of matter. Most matter changes from solid to liquid to gas as its temperature rises, and from gas to liquid to solid as its temperature lowers. However, some solids, such as dry ice, can change directly to a gas without passing through the liquid state. Explain that changing the size of matter, such as by cutting, is also a physical change.

- Tell students that *displacement* uses the Latin prefix *dis-*, meaning "away or off" and the suffix *-ment*, meaning "the result of an action." Ask them to define *displacement* in their own words.

Have students read the selection again on their own.

AFTER READING

Review Graphic Organizers

Answer any questions students have about the reading selection. Then have students complete or review their graphic organizer and share it with the class.

Summarize

Have students work together to come up with either a written or an oral summary of the lesson. Encourage students to use the target vocabulary words as the basis of their summary. Have students share their summary with the class.

My Science Vocabulary

Encourage students to turn to My Science Vocabulary on page 94 of the student book and use the space provided to add other words about properties and changes of matter.

A. *Fill in the blanks with the correct vocabulary word.*

1. the upward force applied by a fluid on objects placed in the fluid

   b u o y a n t   f o r c e

2. a change in the size, shape, or state of matter

   p h y s i c a l   c h a n g e

3. the amount of matter in an object

   m a s s

4. the amount of matter packed into a certain volume

   d e n s i t y

5. the temperature at which a solid changes to a liquid

   m e l t i n g   p o i n t

6. a change in matter that results in different substances

   c h e m i c a l   c h a n g e

7. the temperature at which a liquid changes to a gas

   b o i l i n g   p o i n t

8. the amount of space matter takes up

   v o l u m e

9. the volume of fluid pushed aside by an object placed in the fluid

   d i s p l a c e m e n t

10. the temperature at which a liquid changes to a solid

    f r e e z i n g   p o i n t

B. *Circle the word that makes sense in each sentence. Then write the word.*

1. A change in which one kind of matter changes to one or more new substances is a (chemical change, physical change). _____chemical change_____

2. To learn how tightly packed matter is, you can find its (melting point, density). _____density_____

3. The volume of fluid pushed aside by an object is the object's (buoyant force, displacement). _____displacement_____

4. When you heat a liquid, it changes to a gas at its (melting point, boiling point). _____boiling point_____

5. Objects placed in water seem to lose weight because the water has a (mass, buoyant force). _____buoyant force_____

6. Liters are often used to measure the (volume, freezing point) of a liquid. _____volume_____

7. A solid changes to a liquid at its (melting point, displacement). _____melting point_____

8. During one type of (volume, physical change), heat causes a liquid to change to a gas. _____physical change_____

9. Unlike weight, the (mass, chemical change) of an object does not change when it is moved. _____mass_____

10. When a liquid reaches its (freezing point, boiling point), the temperature is low enough for it to change to a solid. _____freezing point_____

WORD ROOT

The word **mass** comes from the Greek word **maza**, which means "barley cake" or "lump."

ACTIVITIES A–D

Encourage students to complete as many of the activities as possible. Remind students that they may refer to the Glossary at the back of their book as they complete the activities. Students may work independently, in small groups, or as a class. When students are done, discuss the answers for each activity.

Extensions

These extension ideas allow you to reuse or expand upon the activities. Share them with students who complete the activities before other students, or have students do them for additional practice with the target vocabulary words.

A Put the target vocabulary words in columns based on the number of syllables in the word.

B Circle all the nouns in the sentences.

C Rewrite the sentences as questions that can be answered with either a "yes" or "no."

D Choose one sentence you wrote and draw a picture or diagram to illustrate the sentence and show the meaning of the target vocabulary word.

WORD ROOT

Explain that a barley cake was a solid lump of food, so the Greek word *maza* referred specifically to one type of matter. On the other hand, the word *mass* applies to all types of matter as well as all states of matter.

mass   density   displacement   melting point   boiling point
volume   buoyant force   physical change   freezing point   chemical change

C. *Choose the correct vocabulary word to complete each sentence.*

1. During a ____chemical change____ , the particles of matter break apart and form different substances.

2. At its ____freezing point____ , a liquid becomes a solid.

3. A change from a solid to a liquid or a liquid to a gas is a ____physical change____ .

4. Grams are used to measure the ____mass____ of an object.

5. If you divide the mass of an object by its volume, you get the ____density____ of that object.

6. If you place an ice cube in a glass of water, the ice cube's ____displacement____ will be equal to its own volume.

7. If you heat a solid to its ____melting point____ , it turns into a liquid.

8. A fluid has a ____buoyant force____ that causes an object placed in the fluid to seem lighter.

9. To measure the ____volume____ of matter, you need to determine how much space the matter takes up.

10. Heating a liquid will cause it to change to a gas if the liquid reaches its ____boiling point____ .

---

mass   density   displacement   melting point   boiling point
volume   buoyant force   physical change   freezing point   chemical change

Students' answers will vary.

D. *Use each word in a sentence that shows you understand the meaning of the word.*

1. density You can find the density of matter by dividing the mass by the volume.

2. freezing point When you cool a liquid to its freezing point, it becomes a solid.

3. volume The more space matter takes up, the more volume it has.

4. displacement When an object is placed in water, the displacement is the volume of water pushed aside.

5. buoyant force The upward force you feel when you are swimming is the water's buoyant force.

6. physical change When only the state of matter changes, a physical change has taken place.

7. melting point The melting point of a solid is the same temperature as its freezing point.

8. chemical change Energy is always gained or lost during a chemical change.

9. mass How much matter an object has is its mass.

10. boiling point When you heat water to its boiling point, the water turns to a gas.

 Write!

Write your response to the prompt on a separate sheet of paper. Use as many vocabulary words as you can in your writing.

Imagine you are a scientist and you have a solid and a liquid. What tests can you do to learn about the substances?

Write!

Distribute Writing Graphic Organizer: Main Idea and Details Chart, Teacher Guide page 80. Have students work with a partner or in a small group to brainstorm ideas for writing. Tell students to write a main idea for each paragraph they plan to write about their tests in the Main Idea boxes. Have them describe test details and outcomes in the corresponding Details boxes.

Sample Answer

I can measure the mass and volume of the solid and liquid. Then I can calculate the density of each substance by dividing mass by volume. I can place the object in the liquid to see its displacement and test the buoyant force of my liquid.

I can record temperatures of physical changes. If I heat my solid to its melting point, I will also find out its freezing point. I can bring some of this liquid to its boiling point to change it to a gas. I could also try to combine each of my substances with other substances.

TAKE-HOME ACTIVITY

Assign the Take-Home Activity to students for additional practice with the target vocabulary words. The reproducible Take-Home Activity for Lesson 1 is on page 84 of the Teacher Guide.

Properties and Changes of Matter

TAKE HOME 1

mass   density   displacement   melting point   boiling point
volume   buoyant force   physical change   freezing point   chemical change

Use vocabulary words to complete the puzzle.

Properties and Changes of Matter

ACROSS

4 a change creating new substances

6 the volume of fluid pushed aside by an object placed in the fluid

7 the temperature at which a liquid changes to a gas

8 the amount of matter

9 how tightly packed matter is

DOWN

1 how much space matter takes up

2 the temperature at which a liquid changes to a solid

3 a change in the size, shape, or state of matter

5 the temperature at which a solid changes to a liquid

7 the upward force of a fluid

 Tell someone in your family what you have learned about properties and changes of matter.

84   ©Curriculum Associates, LLC Passwords: Science Vocabulary, Physical Science, Lesson 1

LESSON 2

The Structure of Matter

(Student Book pages 10–15)

Lesson Summary A substance can be an element that cannot be broken down into simpler substances by a chemical change or a compound made up of fixed proportions of more than one element. The smallest unit with the properties of an element is an atom. The smallest unit with the properties of a compound is a molecule. At the atomic level, an atom has a center nucleus of positively charged protons and neutral neutrons. Electrons, charged negatively, orbit the nucleus in a sort of cloud.

TARGET VOCABULARY

element a substance that cannot be broken down into simpler substances by a chemical change

compound a substance made up of two or more elements

atom the smallest unit of an element

molecule the smallest unit of a compound

nucleus the central part of an atom

proton an atomic particle with a positive charge

positive charge an electric charge greater than zero

neutron an atomic particle with no electric charge

electron an atomic particle with a negative charge

negative charge an electric charge less than zero

COGNATES

Spanish-speaking students may find a discussion of the similarities and differences between English and Spanish cognates helpful.

English	Spanish
element	elemento
compound	compuesto
atom	átomo
molecule	molécula
nucleus	núcleo
proton	protón
positive charge	carga positiva
neutron	neutrón
electron	electrón
negative charge	carga negativa

BEFORE READING

Activate Prior Knowledge

Ask students what the word *microcosm* means. Explain that *micro-* means "very small" and *-cosm* means "world." Then have students read the introductory paragraph above the title of the lesson. Tell students that the paragraph refers to the microcosm of matter, which is the structure of matter. Ask what smaller things make up all matter. Write students' suggestions on the board and return to them as students read the selection to see if they were correct.

Introduce Target Vocabulary

Tell students they are about to read a selection about the structure of matter. Write the target vocabulary words on the board. Model the pronunciation of each word and have student volunteers repeat the word. Discuss the meaning of each word and, if necessary, write the definition next to the word.

Present Graphic Organizer

Provide each student with a copy of Vocabulary Graphic Organizer: Word Arrow, Teacher Guide page 79. Have students title the arrow *The Structure of Matter*. As they read the lesson, have them write target vocabulary words in the left side of the arrow that refer to the largest units of matter. Moving right, have them add other words to the arrow that refer to smaller and smaller units of matter, ending with the smallest at the right point of the arrow.

Word and Definition Cards
for Lesson 2 are on pages 101 and 102
of the Teacher Guide.

VOCABULARY STRATEGY: Context Clues

Tell students that sometimes writers provide the definition of a new word. Have them find the word *element* and read the sentence that states the definition of *element*: "An **element** is a substance that cannot be broken down into simpler substances by a chemical change." Tell students that words such as *is, are, means,* and *is called* may signal a definition context clue. Have them underline the definition context clues they find as they read the selection and circle the target vocabulary word that is defined.

LESSON 2

element   atom   nucleus   positive charge   electron
compound   molecule   proton   neutron   negative charge

Most objects are made up of billions of smaller things, which are made up of even smaller things. Read this selection to learn more about the structure of matter.

The Structure of Matter

Elements and Compounds

A substance can be an element or a compound. An **element** is a substance that cannot be broken down into simpler substances by a chemical change. A **compound** is a substance made up of two or more elements. A compound has properties that are different from those of its elements. But compounds can be broken down again into the elements they contain by a chemical change.

Gold is an element.

Calcium carbonate is a compound.

Atoms and Molecules

An **atom** is the smallest unit of an element that still has the properties of that element. Every element consists of atoms of the same type. Some elements have one atom, and others have many more.

The smallest unit of a compound that still has the properties of that compound is a **molecule**. A molecule is made up of two or more different types of atoms. All the atoms making up each element in the compound combine to form a molecule.

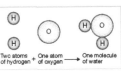
Two atoms of hydrogen + One atom of oxygen → One molecule of water

The Structure of an Atom

Over the years, scientists have created many models of the atom. Today, scientists believe the atom has a center nucleus with tiny particles spinning around it. The **nucleus** is the part of the atom that has the greatest amount of matter, or mass.

The nucleus contains at least one proton. A **proton** is a particle with a positive charge. A **positive charge** is an electric charge greater than zero. An atom may also have one or more neutrons in the nucleus. A **neutron** is a particle with no electric charge.

Electrons orbit the nucleus in a sort of cloud. An **electron** is a particle with a negative charge. A **negative charge** is an electric charge that is less than zero.

Each known element has a specific number of protons in the nucleus and an equal number of electrons in the cloud. The electric charges of the protons and electrons balance.

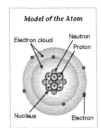
Model of the Atom
Electron cloud — Neutron — Proton — Nucleus — Electron

My Science Vocabulary
Go to page 94 to list other words you have learned about the structure of matter.

The Structure of Matter   10

The Structure of Matter   11

DURING READING

Read the selection aloud to students, stopping at the end of each paragraph or section. Review any words or concepts that students are having trouble with. Remind students that there is a glossary at the back of their book that contains all of the words that appear in boldfaced type in the lesson.

- Explain that *compound* comes from the Latin word *componere*, which means "put together." Although a compound is made up of elements, it does not look or behave like the elements that form it. Far more recognized compounds exist than elements.

- Direct students to the diagram of the atom on page 11. Have students point to the corresponding place on the diagram as volunteers read the labels: *electron, proton, neutron, nucleus, electron cloud.* Then tell them to point to where they would find a positive charge *(where the protons are)* and a negative charge *(where the electrons are).*

- Tell students that the suffix *-on* means "particle." Have them explain the meaning of *neutron* *(a neutral particle, or one with no charge)*; *proton, (a positively charged particle)*; and *electron (a negatively charged particle)*. Encourage students to add these words to the suffix chart on page 100 of their book.

Have students read the selection again on their own.

AFTER READING

Review Graphic Organizers

Answer any questions students have about the reading selection. Then have students complete or review their graphic organizer and share it with the class.

Summarize

Have students work together to come up with either a written or an oral summary of the lesson. Encourage students to use the target vocabulary words as the basis of their summary. Have students share their summary with the class.

My Science Vocabulary

Encourage students to turn to My Science Vocabulary on page 94 of the student book and use the space provided to add other words about the structure of matter.

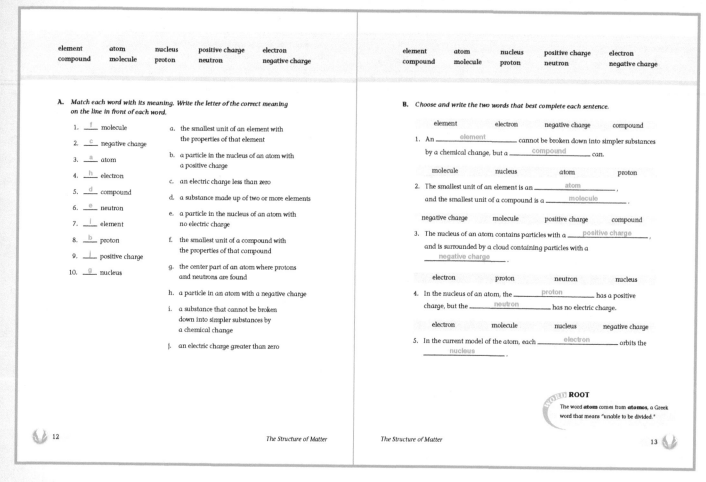

element   atom   nucleus   positive charge   electron
compound   molecule   proton   neutron   negative charge

A. *Match each word with its meaning. Write the letter of the correct meaning on the line in front of each word.*

1. _f_ molecule
2. _c_ negative charge
3. _a_ atom
4. _h_ electron
5. _d_ compound
6. _e_ neutron
7. _i_ element
8. _b_ proton
9. _j_ positive charge
10. _g_ nucleus

a. the smallest unit of an element with the properties of that element
b. a particle in the nucleus of an atom with a positive charge
c. an electric charge less than zero
d. a substance made up of two or more elements
e. a particle in the nucleus of an atom with no electric charge
f. the smallest unit of a compound with the properties of that compound
g. the center part of an atom where protons and neutrons are found
h. a particle in an atom with a negative charge
i. a substance that cannot be broken down into simpler substances by a chemical change
j. an electric charge greater than zero

B. *Choose and write the two words that best complete each sentence.*

element   electron   negative charge   compound

1. An _element_ cannot be broken down into simpler substances by a chemical change, but a _compound_ can.

molecule   nucleus   atom   proton

2. The smallest unit of an element is an _atom_, and the smallest unit of a compound is a _molecule_.

negative charge   molecule   positive charge   compound

3. The nucleus of an atom contains particles with a _positive charge_, and is surrounded by a cloud containing particles with a _negative charge_.

electron   proton   neutron   nucleus

4. In the nucleus of an atom, the _proton_ has a positive charge, but the _neutron_ has no electric charge.

electron   molecule   nucleus   negative charge

5. In the current model of the atom, each _electron_ orbits the _nucleus_.

ROOT
The word *atom* comes from *atomos*, a Greek word that means "unable to be divided."

The Structure of Matter

The Structure of Matter

ACTIVITIES A–D

Encourage students to complete as many of the activities as possible. Remind students that they may refer to the Glossary at the back of their book as they complete the activities. Students may work independently, in small groups, or as a class. When students are done, discuss the answers for each activity.

Extensions

These extension ideas allow you to reuse or expand upon the activities. Share them with students who complete the activities before other students, or have students do them for additional practice with the target vocabulary words.

A Put the target vocabulary words in alphabetical order.

B Draw a diagram that illustrates one of the sentences.

WORD ROOT

Ask students to explain in what way the Greek word *atomos* relates to the meaning of the word *atom*. *(An atom is the smallest unit of an element that cannot be divided and still have the element's properties.)* Then challenge them to explain in what way the word root is not appropriate. *(An atom can be divided into smaller particles called protons, neutrons, and electrons).* Point out that when the word *atom* came into use, scientists did not know about smaller particles.

C Rewrite each pair of sentences as a single sentence that states the same information.

D Write a second sentence that gives more information about the pair of target vocabulary words in each of your sentences.

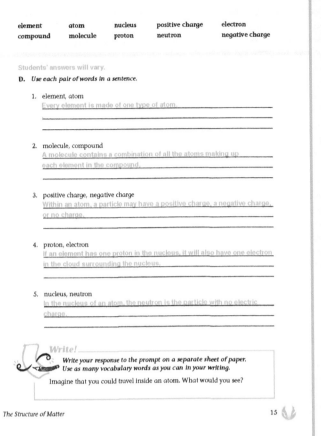

Write!

Distribute Writing Graphic Organizer: Narrative Map, Teacher Guide page 82. Have students work with a partner or in a small group to brainstorm ideas for writing. Students can create a character, or they can be the main character. Setting(s) should include the places they travel to inside the atom. Main events should include what occurs.

Sample Answer

   Inside an atom, I would first visit a sort of cloud that would have one electron or more orbiting the nucleus. Each electron would have a negative charge. As I approached the nucleus, I would see particles with a larger mass. I would find a proton with a positive charge and a neutron with no charge in the nucleus.

TAKE-HOME ACTIVITY

Assign the Take-Home Activity to students for additional practice with the target vocabulary words. The reproducible Take-Home Activity for Lesson 2 is on page 85 of the Teacher Guide.

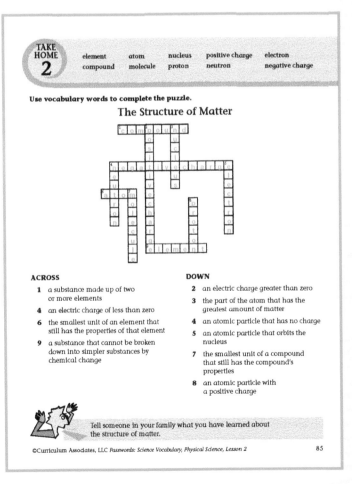

The Structure of Matter

LESSON 3

The Periodic Table of Elements

(Student Book pages 16–21)

Lesson Summary The periodic table groups elements in rows by increasing atomic number. Each element has a unique chemical symbol and atomic number. The atomic mass, or amount of matter, is roughly equal to the number of protons and neutrons in the nucleus. The elements grouped in columns on the periodic table have similar chemical properties. Hydrogen is at the top left. Metals are on the left, nonmetals on the right, and a zigzag line of metalloids lies between them. Noble gases, including helium, form the group at the far right.

TARGET VOCABULARY

periodic table a grouping of elements by properties

chemical symbol an abbreviation for an element

atomic number the number of protons in the nucleus

atomic mass the amount of matter in an atom

chemical property how an element acts with other elements

hydrogen the gas with the atomic number 1

nonmetal an element with no metallic properties

metalloid an element with some metallic and nonmetallic properties

noble gas a gas that does not normally combine with other elements

helium the noble gas with the atomic number 2

COGNATES

Spanish-speaking students may find a discussion of the similarities and differences between English and Spanish cognates helpful.

English	Spanish
periodic table	tabla periódica
chemical symbol	símbolo químico
atomic number	número atómico
atomic mass	masa atómica
chemical property	propiedad química
hydrogen	hidrógeno
noble gas	gas noble
helium	helio

BEFORE READING

Activate Prior Knowledge

Tell students that *ferrum*, *kalium*, *aurum*, and *argentium* are the Latin names for iron, potassium, gold, and silver. Explain that when they see a chemical symbol for an element that doesn't make sense to them, such as *Fe* for iron, the abbreviation may have come from the name of the element in a different language, such as Latin, Greek, or Arabic.

Introduce Target Vocabulary

Tell students they are about to read a selection about the periodic table of elements. Write the target vocabulary words on the board. Model the pronunciation of each word and have student volunteers repeat the word. Discuss the meaning of each word and, if necessary, write the definition next to the word.

Present Graphic Organizer

Provide each student with a copy of Vocabulary Graphic Organizer: Word Web, Teacher Guide page 76. Have students write *The Periodic Table of Elements* in the center circle of the web. As they read the lesson, have students group related target vocabulary words in the outer circles. Have them define each of these words. Tell them they may add circles, if necessary.

Word and Definition Cards
for Lesson 3 are on pages 103 and 104
of the Teacher Guide.

VOCABULARY STRATEGY: Roots

Tell students that common roots can help them determine the meaning of unknown words. Have students find the two target vocabulary words that include *metal* (*nonmetal, metalloid*). Point out that the prefix *non-* means "not." Ask what a *nonmetal* is (*a substance that is not a metal*). Tell students that the suffix *-oid* means "a likeness to." Ask what a *metalloid* is (*a substance that is somewhat like a metal but also like a nonmetal*). Have students list other words that include *metal* (*metallic, nonmetallic, metalwork,* and so on).

The Periodic Table of Elements

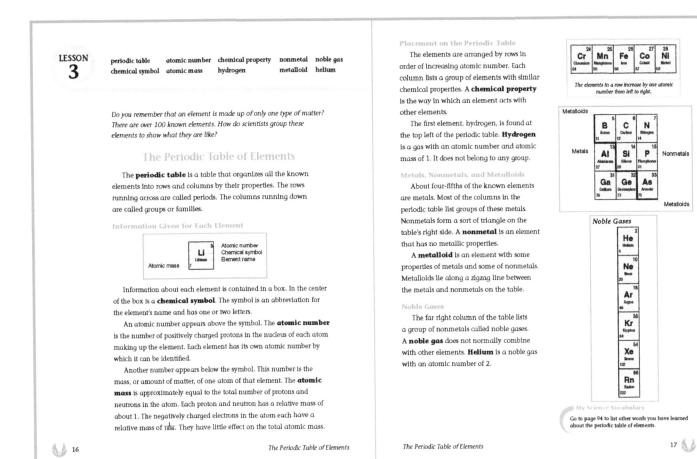

LESSON 3

periodic table   atomic number   chemical property   nonmetal   noble gas
chemical symbol   atomic mass   hydrogen   metalloid   helium

Do you remember that an element is made up of only one type of matter? There are over 100 known elements. How do scientists group these elements to show what they are like?

The Periodic Table of Elements

The **periodic table** is a table that organizes all the known elements into rows and columns by their properties. The rows running across are called periods. The columns running down are called groups or families.

Information Given for Each Element

Li — Atomic number, Chemical symbol, Element name; Atomic mass

Information about each element is contained in a box. In the center of the box is a **chemical symbol**. The symbol is an abbreviation for the element's name and has one or two letters.

An atomic number appears above the symbol. The **atomic number** is the number of positively charged protons in the nucleus of each atom making up the element. Each element has its own atomic number by which it can be identified.

Another number appears below the symbol. This number is the mass, or amount of matter, of one atom of that element. The **atomic mass** is approximately equal to the total number of protons and neutrons in the atom. Each proton and neutron has a relative mass of about 1. The negatively charged electrons in the atom each have a relative mass of $\frac{1}{1836}$. They have little effect on the total atomic mass.

16   *The Periodic Table of Elements*

Placement on the Periodic Table

The elements are arranged by rows in order of increasing atomic number. Each column lists a group of elements with similar chemical properties. A **chemical property** is the way in which an element acts with other elements.

The first element, hydrogen, is found at the top left of the periodic table. **Hydrogen** is a gas with an atomic number and atomic mass of 1. It does not belong to any group.

The elements in a row increase by one atomic number from left to right.

Metals, Nonmetals, and Metalloids

About four-fifths of the known elements are metals. Most of the columns in the periodic table list groups of these metals. Nonmetals form a sort of triangle on the table's right side. A **nonmetal** is an element that has no metallic properties.

A **metalloid** is an element with some properties of metals and some of nonmetals. Metalloids lie along a zigzag line between the metals and nonmetals on the table.

Noble Gases

The far right column of the table lists a group of nonmetals called noble gases. A **noble gas** does not normally combine with other elements. **Helium** is a noble gas with an atomic number of 2.

My Science Vocabulary
Go to page 94 to list other words you have learned about the periodic table of elements.

The Periodic Table of Elements   17

DURING READING

Read the selection aloud to students, stopping at the end of each paragraph or section. Review any words or concepts that students are having trouble with. Remind students that there is a glossary at the back of their book that contains all of the words that appear in boldfaced type in the lesson.

- Provide each student with a copy of the complete periodic table of elements. Images of the periodic table are available online. Have students refer to the table as they complete the lesson.

- Direct students to the diagram of the periodic-table box for lithium on page 16. Have students point to the information that is labeled as you read the labels aloud.

- Point out that *hydrogen* combines the prefix *hydro-*, which refers to water, and *-gen*, which means "birth or origin." Ask students how hydrogen probably got its name; if they need help, remind them that water is H_2O. (*Hydrogen joins with oxygen to create water.*) Ask students to list other words that use the prefix *hydro-* (hydrofoil, hydroplane, hydroelectric, etc.). Encourage students to add these words to the prefix chart on page 100 of their book.

Have students read the selection again on their own.

AFTER READING

Review Graphic Organizers

Answer any questions students have about the reading selection. Then have students complete or review their graphic organizer and share it with the class.

Summarize

Have students work together to come up with either a written or an oral summary of the lesson. Encourage students to use the target vocabulary words as the basis of their summary. Have students share their summary with the class.

My Science Vocabulary

Encourage students to turn to My Science Vocabulary on page 94 of the student book and use the space provided to add other words about the periodic table of elements.

The Periodic Table of Elements

25

A. *Fill in the blanks with the correct vocabulary word.*

1. the mass of an atom
   a t o m i c   m a s s

2. a one- or two-letter abbreviation for an element's name
   c h e m i c a l   s y m b o l

3. a table that organizes all the known elements by their properties
   p e r i o d i c   t a b l e

4. the way in which an element acts with other elements
   c h e m i c a l   p r o p e r t y

5. a gas with an atomic number and atomic mass of 1
   h y d r o g e n

6. an element that has no metallic properties
   n o n m e t a l

7. an element that has some properties of metals and some of nonmetals
   m e t a l l o i d

8. a noble gas with an atomic number of 2
   h e l i u m

9. the number of protons in the nucleus of an atom
   a t o m i c   n u m b e r

10. any gas that is a nonmetal
    n o b l e   g a s

B. *Circle the word that makes sense in each sentence. Then write the word.*

1. To find a (chemical property, chemical symbol) of an element, learn how it acts with other elements. _____ chemical property

2. One property of a (noble gas, nonmetal) is that it does not normally combine with other elements. _____ noble gas

3. The number of protons in the nucleus of an atom determines the (chemical symbol, atomic number) of an element. _____ atomic number

4. The element found at the top left corner of the periodic table is the gas (helium, hydrogen). _____ hydrogen

5. The elements are arranged in rows and columns in the (atomic mass, periodic table). _____ periodic table

6. The amount of matter in an atom is the (atomic mass, noble gas). _____ atomic mass

7. The periodic table uses a (chemical symbol, metalloid) to represent the name of each element. _____ chemical symbol

8. On the periodic table, each (chemical property, nonmetal) can be found on the right, in a sort of triangle. _____ nonmetal

9. The element with an atomic number of 2 is a noble gas called (helium, metalloid). _____ helium

10. An element with some metallic and some nonmetallic properties is a (metalloid, noble gas). _____ metalloid

ROOT

The word **periodic** comes from the Latin root **periodus**, which means "a period, or interval, of time."

ACTIVITIES A–D

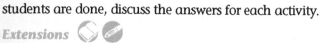

Encourage students to complete as many of the activities as possible. Remind students that they may refer to the Glossary at the back of their book as they complete the activities. Students may work independently, in small groups, or as a class. When students are done, discuss the answers for each activity.

Extensions

These extension ideas allow you to reuse or expand upon the activities. Share them with students who complete the activities before other students, or have students do them for additional practice with the target vocabulary words.

A Write a complete sentence for each target vocabulary word and its definition.

B Renumber the sentences so that they are in alphabetical order by the target vocabulary words.

WORD ROOT

Explain to students that the meaning of *periodus*, "a period, or interval, of time," relates to the periodic table because properties of elements on the periodic table repeat at given intervals. For this usage, time is taken not literally, in the sense of a number of minutes, but figuratively, in the sense of repeating regularly.

C Some of the target vocabulary words contain smaller words; for example, *atomic number* contains the words *atom, to,* and *numb.* Make a list of smaller words in the target vocabulary words. Put a star next to a smaller word whose meaning relates to the larger word, such as *atom* in *atomic.*

D Copy a box from the periodic table that relates to each sentence you wrote. Write a caption to explain how the box relates to your sentence.

periodic table   atomic number   chemical property   nonmetal   noble gas
chemical symbol   atomic mass   hydrogen   metalloid   helium

C. *Choose the correct vocabulary word to complete each sentence.*

1. Each element in the periodic table is represented by a __chemical symbol__ that has one or two letters.

2. An element that is a __metalloid__ lies along a zigzag line between the metals and nonmetals on the periodic table.

3. The gas __hydrogen__ is the first element in the periodic table.

4. Each element in the group of nonmetals at the far right of the periodic table is a __noble gas__.

5. On the right side of the periodic table, you can find a __nonmetal__, which has no metallic properties.

6. The way an element behaves with another element is a __chemical property__.

7. The columns in the __periodic table__ contain groups of elements with like properties.

8. The noble gas with the lowest atomic number is __helium__.

9. The number of protons in the nucleus of an atom gives the element its __atomic number__.

10. An element with 2 protons and 2 neutrons has an __atomic mass__ of about 4.

periodic table   atomic number   chemical property   nonmetal   noble gas
chemical symbol   atomic mass   hydrogen   metalloid   helium

Students' answers will vary.

D. *Use each pair of words in a sentence.*

1. periodic table, chemical property
   In each column on the periodic table, most of the elements share more than one chemical property.

2. atomic number, chemical symbol
   On the periodic table, the chemical symbol stands for the element's name and the atomic number tells how many protons an atom has.

3. atomic mass, hydrogen
   The atomic mass of hydrogen is 1.

4. nonmetal, metalloid
   A nonmetal has no properties of metals, but a metalloid has properties of both metals and nonmetals.

5. helium, noble gas
   The gas helium is a noble gas, so it does not normally combine with other elements.

 Write!
Write your response to the prompt on a separate sheet of paper. Use as many vocabulary words as you can in your writing.

In your own words, describe how the periodic table organizes and identifies Earth's elements.

Write!

Distribute Writing Graphic Organizer: Main Idea and Details Chart, Teacher Guide page 80. Tell students to write a main idea about how the periodic table organizes elements in the first Main Idea box. Have them write a main idea about how the periodic table identifies elements in the second Main Idea box. Have them write details to support their main ideas in the corresponding Details boxes.

Sample Answer

On the periodic table, elements are organized by atomic number. The chemical symbol of the element makes the table easy to read. The atomic mass can help you find the average number of neutrons in the nucleus.

Elements in vertical groups share at least one chemical property. Nonmetals are in a triangle at the right and metalloids are along the zigzag line. Hydrogen is in the top left corner. Helium is in the top right corner.

TAKE-HOME ACTIVITY

Assign the Take-Home Activity to students for additional practice with the target vocabulary words. The reproducible Take-Home Activity for Lesson 3 is on page 86 of the Teacher Guide.

The Periodic Table of Elements

TAKE HOME 3

periodic table   atomic number   chemical property   nonmetal   noble gas
chemical symbol   atomic mass   hydrogen   metalloid   helium

Use vocabulary words to complete the puzzle.

The Periodic Table of Elements

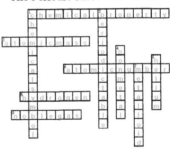

ACROSS

1 the way an element acts with other elements
3 the amount of matter of an atom
6 the number of protons in the nucleus of an atom
8 the gas with an atomic number of 1
9 a type of gas that does not normally combine with other elements

DOWN

1 the one- or two-letter abbreviation for an element
2 a chart that groups elements by properties
4 an element with no metallic properties
5 the noble gas with an atomic number of 2
7 an element with some properties of metals and some of nonmetals

 Tell someone in your family what you have learned about the periodic table of elements.

The Periodic Table of Elements

LESSON 4

The Science of Chemistry

(Student Book pages 22–27)

TARGET VOCABULARY

chemistry the study of matter and its changes

chemical bond the force joining atoms in a compound

chemical reaction a change in which bonds are broken or made

reactant a raw material of a chemical reaction

product an end result of a chemical reaction

chemical formula a description, using numbers and symbols, of the atoms in a compound

chemical equation a description, using numbers and symbols, of a chemical reaction

solution a mixture that is the same throughout

solvent in a solution, the substance that dissolves the other substance

solute in a solution, the substance that is dissolved

COGNATES

Spanish-speaking students may find a discussion of the similarities and differences between English and Spanish cognates helpful.

English	Spanish
chemistry	química
chemical reaction	reacción química
product	producto
chemical formula	fórmula química
chemical equation	ecuación química
solution	solución
solvent	disolvente
solute	soluto

VOCABULARY STRATEGY: Word Families

Explain to students that many words belong to a "family," or a group of words with a common root. Ask students to find three target vocabulary words that come from the root *solvere*, which means "to loosen, divide, or cut apart" (*solution, solvent, solute*). Point out that these words are all nouns. Ask students to explain how the three nouns are different (*solution is the overall mixture; solvent is the substance that*

Lesson Summary Chemistry is the study of matter and how it changes. Chemical bonds link atoms of elements to form compounds. A chemical reaction is a change in which bonds are made or broken. The reactant of a chemical reaction includes all the raw materials that react to form the new product or products. Scientists write chemical equations of reactions using chemical formulas. Instead of reacting, some elements and compounds form solutions in which the solvent dissolves the solute.

BEFORE READING

Activate Prior Knowledge

Have students read the paragraph above the title of the lesson. Encourage them to share stories of movie scenes they have seen that are like the one described. Then have them answer the question. Accept all answers. Then have students read the title of the lesson. Lead them to realize that chemistry explains some apparently fantastic reactions of substances.

Introduce Target Vocabulary

Tell students they are about to read a selection about the science of chemistry. Write the target vocabulary words on the board. Model the pronunciation of each word and have student volunteers repeat the word. Discuss the meaning of each word and, if necessary, write the definition next to the word.

Present Graphic Organizer

Have students work with a partner. Provide each pair with a copy of Vocabulary Graphic Organizer: Word Web, Teacher Guide page 76. Have students write *Chemistry* in the center circle of the web. As they read the lesson, have students group related target vocabulary words in the outer circles. Have them write a phrase next to each circle that explains why they grouped the words together.

Word and Definition Cards
for Lesson 4 are on pages 105 and 106
of the Teacher Guide.

dissolves the other substance; solute is the substance that is dissolved). Point out that *dissolve* is also from the same root but uses the prefix *dis-* meaning "apart." Have students list other words from the same family (*solve, solvable, soluble, dissolved, dissolving, dissolution, absolve, and so on*). Encourage students to add these words to the root words chart on page 99 and the prefix chart on page 100 of their book.

The Science of Chemistry

chemistry   reactant   chemical equation   solvent
chemical bond   product   solution   solute
chemical reaction   chemical formula

A scientist in a movie mixes two substances, and they change color, give off huge clouds of smoke, or form a slimy mass. Is this just fantasy? Read this selection to learn about chemistry.

The Science of Chemistry

The science of **chemistry** is the study of matter and how it changes. A chemist examines elements and compounds, and how they react when they are brought together.

An element is made of only one kind of atom. A compound is made up of more than one element.

Chemical Bonds

The atoms of different elements can combine in many ways to make compounds. When atoms combine, they form chemical bonds. A **chemical bond** is a force of attraction that holds together the atoms in a compound. Every compound is held together by chemical bonds.

A chemist often wears safety equipment, such as gloves, a mask, and goggles.

Reactants and Products

When elements or compounds are brought together, a chemical reaction may occur. A **chemical reaction** is a change in which chemical bonds are broken or made, forming one or more new substances.

In a chemical reaction, each substance that is brought together and reacts is called a **reactant**. It is one of the raw materials of the chemical reaction. Each substance that forms as a result of the chemical reaction is called a **product**. It is one of the end results of the chemical reaction.

Chemical Formulas and Equations

A chemical reaction can be written out. Chemical symbols, or abbreviations, stand for the elements that make up a compound. Numbers show how many atoms of each element make up a molecule of the compound. This set of symbols and numbers that shows what a compound is made of is a **chemical formula**.

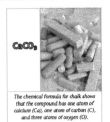
$CaCO_3$

The chemical formula for chalk shows that the compound has one atom of calcium (Ca), one atom of carbon (C), and three atoms of oxygen (O).

A **chemical equation** is an expression that uses chemical formulas and symbols to show the reactants and products of a chemical reaction. The reactants are on the left in the equation and the products are on the right.

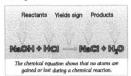

| Reactants | Yields sign | Products |

$$NaOH + HCl \longrightarrow NaCl + H_2O$$

The chemical equation shows that no atoms are gained or lost during a chemical reaction.

Solutions

Some elements and compounds come together without causing a chemical reaction. One example is a **solution**, a kind of mixture in which one or more substances seem to disappear into another substance. The mixture is the same throughout. The substance that takes in, or dissolves, another substance is called the **solvent**. The substance that is dissolved is the **solute**.

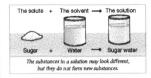

The solute   +   The solvent ⟶ The solution
Sugar   +   Water ⟶ Sugar water

The substances in a solution may look different, but they do not form new substances.

My Science Vocabulary

Go to page 95 to list other words you have learned about the science of chemistry.

DURING READING

Read the selection aloud to students, stopping at the end of each paragraph or section. Review any words or concepts that students are having trouble with. Remind students that there is a glossary at the back of their book that contains all of the words that appear in boldfaced type in the lesson.

- Students may be interested to learn that *chemist* comes from *chimist* which is short for Medieval *alchymista*, or *alchemist*. One goal of an alchemist was to change base metal into gold.

- Discuss the chemical equation on page 23. Explain that a subscript after a symbol means that there are that number of atoms of that element; for example, H_2 is 2 atoms of hydrogen. Show students that the equation balances; the total number of atoms of each element on each side is the same. Tell students that if more than one molecule of a substance is needed, the number is placed before the symbol or formula.

- Explain to students that all three phases of matter—solids, liquids, and gases—can form solutions. An alloy is a solid formed by the mixing of two melted metals. Snow is a solid in a gas, whereas fog is a liquid in a gas.

Have students read the selection again on their own.

AFTER READING

Review Graphic Organizers

Answer any questions students have about the reading selection. Then have students complete or review their graphic organizer and share it with the class.

Summarize

Have students work together to come up with either a written or an oral summary of the lesson. Encourage students to use the target vocabulary words as the basis of their summary. Have students share their summary with the class.

My Science Vocabulary

Encourage students to turn to My Science Vocabulary on page 95 of the student book and use the space provided to add other words about the science of chemistry.

chemistry   reactant   chemical equation   solvent
chemical bond   product   solution   solute
chemical reaction   chemical formula

A. Match each word with its meaning. Write the letter of the correct meaning on the line in front of each word.

1. __e__ solvent
2. __h__ chemical bond
3. __d__ chemistry
4. __j__ solute
5. __i__ chemical reaction
6. __g__ product
7. __b__ chemical formula
8. __c__ solution
9. __f__ chemical equation
10. __a__ reactant

a. an element or a compound that is a raw material in a chemical reaction

b. a set of symbols and numbers that shows the elements making up a compound and the number of atoms in each element

c. a mixture in which one or more substances are dissolved in another substance

d. the study of matter and how it changes

e. a substance that dissolves another substance to form a solution

f. an expression that uses chemical formulas and symbols to show the reactants and products of a chemical reaction

g. each substance that is formed during a chemical reaction

h. a force of attraction that holds together the atoms in a compound

i. a change in which chemical bonds are formed or broken to create new substances

j. a substance that is dissolved in another substance, forming a solution

24   *The Science of Chemistry*

---

chemistry   reactant   chemical equation   solvent
chemical bond   product   solution   solute
chemical reaction   chemical formula

B. Circle the word that makes sense in each sentence. Then write the word.

1. Sugar dissolves in water, forming a (reactant, **solution**). ___solution___

2. To show the type of elements in a compound and how many atoms they have, you can use a (**chemical formula**, solute). ___chemical formula___

3. The study of elements and compounds and how they react is the science of (solution, **chemistry**). ___chemistry___

4. Each atom in a compound is held to another by a (chemical equation, **chemical bond**). ___chemical bond___

5. Reactants are listed on the left side of a (**chemical equation**, chemical bond) and products are on the right. ___chemical equation___

6. Salt is the (**solute**, solvent) that dissolves in water to form a solution of salt water. ___solute___

7. A new substance that forms from a chemical reaction is a (**product**, solvent) of that reaction. ___product___

8. When you dissolve sugar in water, the water is the (**solvent**, reactant). ___solvent___

9. Each raw material for a chemical reaction is a (**reactant**, product). ___reactant___

10. Chemical bonds are formed or broken during a (chemical formula, **chemical reaction**). ___chemical reaction___

ROOT
The word **product** is based on the Latin word **producere**, which means "to produce or to make."

The Science of Chemistry   25

ACTIVITIES A–D

Encourage students to complete as many of the activities as possible. Remind students that they may refer to the Glossary at the back of their book as they complete the activities. Students may work independently, in small groups, or as a class. When students are done, discuss the answers for each activity.

Extensions

These extension ideas allow you to reuse or expand upon the activities. Share them with students who complete the activities before other students, or have students do them for additional practice with the target vocabulary words.

A Turn each matching word and meaning into a complete sentence.

B Underline the words in each sentence that were the clues you used to choose the correct answer.

WORD ROOT

Ask students how the root of *producere* relates to the word *product (the product is what is produced from a chemical reaction).* Explain that the product of a chemical reaction includes all the elements or compounds formed during the chemical reaction. A product may be one substance or many substances. Ask students to list other words that use the root *producere (produce, productive, producer, production).*

C Choose one pair of sentences and draw a picture or a diagram to illustrate the meaning of the target vocabulary word.

D For each of your sentences, write a second sentence that adds more information.

chemistry reactant chemical equation solvent
chemical bond product solution solute
chemical reaction chemical formula

C. *Write the vocabulary word that best completes each pair of sentences.*

1. In a solution, the substance dissolved is a ___solute___ .
   The solvent dissolves the ___solute___ .

2. A chemical reaction is shown in a ___chemical equation___ .
   A ___chemical equation___ lists products on the right.

3. When atoms combine, they form a ___chemical bond___ .
   A ___chemical bond___ is a force of attraction between atoms.

4. The science of ___chemistry___ is the study of matter.
   How matter changes is part of the study of ___chemistry___ .

5. You can write a ___chemical formula___ to show what a compound is made of.
   A ___chemical formula___ shows how many atoms of each element are in one molecule of a compound.

6. A mixture that is the same throughout is a ___solution___ .
   A ___solution___ consists of a solvent and a solute.

7. A raw material for a chemical reaction is a ___reactant___ .
   A ___reactant___ may help form one or more new products.

8. A solution has a solute and a ___solvent___ .
   The solute dissolves into the ___solvent___ .

9. During a ___chemical reaction___ , chemical bonds break or form.
   New products form from a ___chemical reaction___ .

10. A new substance made by a chemical reaction is a ___product___ .
    Reactants form at least one new ___product___ .

 26

The Science of Chemistry

---

chemistry reactant chemical equation solvent
chemical bond product solution solute
chemical reaction chemical formula

D. *Use each word in a sentence that shows you understand the meaning of the word.*

1. chemical bond ___A chemical bond holds together the atoms in a compound.___

2. chemical equation ___A chemical equation uses chemical formulas and symbols to show a chemical reaction.___

3. solvent ___If a substance forms a solution in water, the water is the solvent.___

4. reactant ___Each of the substances that come together and cause a chemical reaction is called a reactant.___

5. chemistry ___In chemistry, scientists study how elements and compounds react with each other.___

6. solute ___The solute is the substance that dissolves in the solvent.___

7. chemical formula ___A chemical formula shows which elements are in a compound and how many atoms make up one molecule of the compound.___

8. solution ___A solution is a mixture in which elements and compounds come together without causing a chemical reaction.___

9. product ___Every chemical reaction has at least one new product.___

10. chemical reaction ___During a chemical reaction, bonds between atoms are made or broken.___

 Write!
Write your response to the prompt on a separate sheet of paper. Use as many vocabulary words as you can in your writing.

Imagine you work as a chemist. Tell what kinds of experiments you might do. Describe what happens.

The Science of Chemistry

27

Write!

Distribute Writing Graphic Organizer: Sequence Chart, Teacher Guide page 83. In the first box, students should write their first experiment. In the following boxes, they should write in order other experiments they would perform and what happens.

Sample Answer

I enjoy my work with chemistry. Yesterday, I worked with a solution. The solute was a salt, and the solvent was water. The solute appeared to dissolve completely in the solvent. Today, I will record what that solution looks like after 12 hours.

Today, I have several reactants that I know will react to form a new product. I have written the chemical equation for this reaction on my chalkboard, using the formula for the compounds I have and for those I expect will form. I want to see what will happen when the chemical bond that holds the compound together is broken.

TAKE-HOME ACTIVITY

Assign the Take-Home Activity to students for additional practice with the target vocabulary words. The reproducible Take-Home Activity for Lesson 4 is on page 87 of the Teacher Guide.

The Science of Chemistry

TAKE HOME 4

chemistry reactant chemical equation solvent
chemical bond product solution solute
chemical reaction chemical formula

Use vocabulary words to complete the puzzle.

The Science of Chemistry

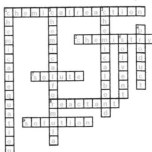

ACROSS

1 a change in which chemical bonds are broken or made

5 the study of matter and how it changes

7 the substance that dissolves in the solvent

8 the raw material of a chemical reaction

9 a mixture that is the same throughout

DOWN

1 an expression that uses chemical formulas and symbols to show the reactants and products of a chemical reaction

2 the symbols and numbers that show what a compound is made of

3 the force that joins atoms in a compound

4 the substance that forms as a result of a chemical reaction

6 the substance that dissolves another substance in a solution

 Tell someone in your family what you have learned about the science of chemistry.

©Curriculum Associates, LLC *Passwords: Science Vocabulary, Physical Science, Lesson 4* 87

LESSON 5

Acids and Bases

(Student Book pages 28–33)

TARGET VOCABULARY

acid a substance that produces hydrogen ions in water

ion an atom or atoms with an electric charge

soluble able to be dissolved

base a substance that produces hydroxide ions in water

alkaline basic, not acidic

pH a measure of how acidic or alkaline a solution is

neutral neither acidic nor alkaline

indicator a substance that changes color in an acid or a base

litmus paper an indicator made of treated paper

neutralize to make neutral

COGNATES

Spanish-speaking students may find a discussion of the similarities and differences between English and Spanish cognates helpful.

English	Spanish
acid	ácido
ion	ion
soluble	soluble
base	base
alkaline	alcalino
neutral	neutro
indicator	indicador
paper	papel
neutralize	neutralizar

Lesson Summary An ion is an atom or group of atoms with an electric charge. An acid gives up hydrogen ions in solution with water, whereas a base, or alkaline substance, produces hydroxide ions. Solutions can be measured for how acidic or alkaline they are, using the pH scale. An indicator, such as litmus paper, is a substance that changes color to indicate the presence of an acid or a base. When an acid and a base react together, they produce a salt and water. The acid and base are neutralized by this reaction.

BEFORE READING

Activate Prior Knowledge

Ask students if they have ever seen advertisements or labels on products that say "pH balanced," or bring in some ads or product labels to show students. Have students guess what this phrase means and why being pH balanced might be important for the type of products on which the wording appears.

Introduce Target Vocabulary

Tell students they are about to read a selection about acids and bases. Write the target vocabulary words on the board. Model the pronunciation of each word and have student volunteers repeat the word. Discuss the meaning of each word and, if necessary, write the definition next to the word.

Present Graphic Organizer

Provide each student with a copy of Vocabulary Graphic Organizer: Four Square, Teacher Guide page 78. Have students choose or assign each student a target vocabulary word. Have students write their word in the center. As they read the lesson, students should add information about the vocabulary word to the graphic organizer.

Word and Definition Cards
for Lesson 5 are on pages 107 and 108
of the Teacher Guide.

VOCABULARY STRATEGY: Suffixes

Remind students that a suffix is a letter or letters added to the end of a word. Tell students that the suffix *-ize*, which means "to make or cause to be," is used to change some adjectives and nouns into verbs. Ask students to find the target vocabulary word ending in the suffix *-ize (neutralize)* and the target vocabulary word that it is formed from *(neutral)*. Ask students to define *neutral* and *neutralize*. (*Neutral* means "not acid or base"; *neutralize* means "to make into something that is not acid or base.") Challenge students to list other verbs ending in *-ize (alphabetize, familiarize, motorize, vaporize, realize, finalize, visualize, materialize, fertilize, symbolize, characterize).* Encourage students to add these words to the suffix chart on page 100 of their book.

Acids and Bases

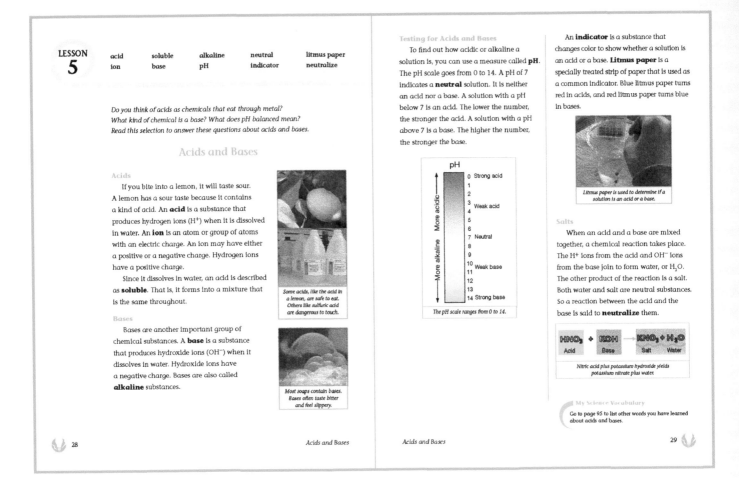

LESSON 5

acid soluble alkaline neutral litmus paper
ion base pH indicator neutralize

Do you think of acids as chemicals that eat through metal?
What kind of chemical is a base? What does pH balanced mean?
Read this selection to answer these questions about acids and bases.

Acids and Bases

Acids

If you bite into a lemon, it will taste sour. A lemon has a sour taste because it contains a kind of acid. An **acid** is a substance that produces hydrogen ions (H^+) when it is dissolved in water. An **ion** is an atom or group of atoms with an electric charge. An ion may have either a positive or a negative charge. Hydrogen ions have a positive charge.

Since it dissolves in water, an acid is described as **soluble**. That is, it forms into a mixture that is the same throughout.

Bases

Bases are another important group of chemical substances. A **base** is a substance that produces hydroxide ions (OH^-) when it dissolves in water. Hydroxide ions have a negative charge. Bases are also called **alkaline** substances.

Some acids, like the acid in a lemon, are safe to eat. Others like sulfuric acid are dangerous to touch.

Most soaps contain bases. Bases often taste bitter and feel slippery.

Testing for Acids and Bases

To find out how acidic or alkaline a solution is, you can use a measure called **pH**. The pH scale goes from 0 to 14. A pH of 7 indicates a **neutral** solution. It is neither an acid nor a base. A solution with a pH below 7 is an acid. The lower the number, the stronger the acid. A solution with a pH above 7 is a base. The higher the number, the stronger the base.

pH

More acidic → / More alkaline →

0 Strong acid
1
2
3 Weak acid
4
5
6
7 Neutral
8
9
10 Weak base
11
12
13
14 Strong base

The pH scale ranges from 0 to 14.

An **indicator** is a substance that changes color to show whether a solution is an acid or a base. **Litmus paper** is a specially treated strip of paper that is used as a common indicator. Blue litmus paper turns red in acids, and red litmus paper turns blue in bases.

Litmus paper is used to determine if a solution is an acid or a base.

Salts

When an acid and a base are mixed together, a chemical reaction takes place. The H^+ ions from the acid and OH^- ions from the base join to form water, or H_2O. The other product of the reaction is a salt. Both water and salt are neutral substances. So a reaction between the acid and the base is said to **neutralize** them.

$$HNO_3 + KOH \rightarrow KNO_3 + H_2O$$

Acid + Base → Salt + Water

Nitric acid plus potassium hydroxide yields potassium nitrate plus water.

My Science Vocabulary
Go to page 95 to list other words you have learned about acids and bases.

28 Acids and Bases Acids and Bases 29

DURING READING

Read the selection aloud to students, stopping at the end of each paragraph or section. Review any words or concepts that students are having trouble with. Remind students that there is a glossary at the back of their book that contains all of the words that appear in boldfaced type in the lesson.

- Tell students that pH stands for "potential hydrogen," referring to the hydrogen ions.

- Tell students that the suffix *-or* means "one that does," so an *indicator* is "something that indicates." Explain that litmus paper is an indicator that uses an organic compound from a species of lichen. The compound was originally used as a dye.

- Direct students' attention to the chemical equation for a neutralization reaction at the bottom of page 29. Point out that the chemical reaction of an acid and a base results in a salt and water. Explain to students that table salt is only one type of salt. Ask if students know what acid and base react to form table salt, or NaCl (*acid: chlorine; base: sodium*).

Have students read the selection again on their own.

AFTER READING

Review Graphic Organizers

Answer any questions students have about the reading selection. Then have students complete or review their graphic organizer and share it with the class.

Summarize

Have students work together to come up with either a written or an oral summary of the lesson. Encourage students to use the target vocabulary words as the basis of their summary. Have students share their summary with the class.

My Science Vocabulary

Encourage students to turn to My Science Vocabulary on page 95 of the student book and use the space provided to add other words about acids and bases.

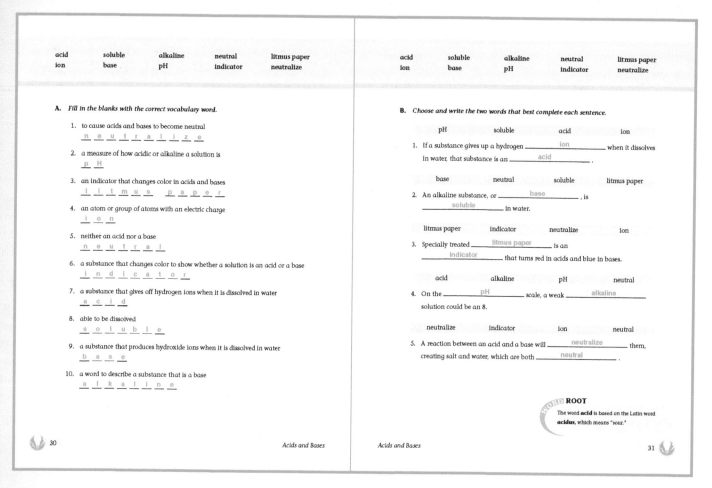

Word bank (repeated on both pages):

acid soluble alkaline neutral litmus paper
ion base pH indicator neutralize

A. Fill in the blanks with the correct vocabulary word.

1. to cause acids and bases to become neutral
   n e u t r a l i z e
2. a measure of how acidic or alkaline a solution is
   p H
3. an indicator that changes color in acids and bases
   l i t m u s   p a p e r
4. an atom or group of atoms with an electric charge
   i o n
5. neither an acid nor a base
   n e u t r a l
6. a substance that changes color to show whether a solution is an acid or a base
   i n d i c a t o r
7. a substance that gives off hydrogen ions when it is dissolved in water
   a c i d
8. able to be dissolved
   s o l u b l e
9. a substance that produces hydroxide ions when it is dissolved in water
   b a s e
10. a word to describe a substance that is a base
    a l k a l i n e

B. Choose and write the two words that best complete each sentence.

pH   soluble   acid   ion

1. If a substance gives up a hydrogen ___ion___ when it dissolves in water, that substance is an ___acid___.

base   neutral   soluble   litmus paper

2. An alkaline substance, or ___base___, is ___soluble___ in water.

litmus paper   indicator   neutralize   ion

3. Specially treated ___litmus paper___ is an ___indicator___ that turns red in acids and blue in bases.

acid   alkaline   pH   neutral

4. On the ___pH___ scale, a weak ___alkaline___ solution could be an 8.

neutralize   indicator   ion   neutral

5. A reaction between an acid and a base will ___neutralize___ them, creating salt and water, which are both ___neutral___.

ROOT
The word **acid** is based on the Latin word **acidus**, which means "sour."

ACTIVITIES A–D

Encourage students to complete as many of the activities as possible. Remind students that they may refer to the Glossary at the back of their book as they complete the activities. Students may work independently, in small groups, or as a class. When students are done, discuss the answers for each activity.

Extensions

These extension ideas allow you to reuse or expand upon the activities. Share them with students who complete the activities before other students, or have students do them for additional practice with the target vocabulary words.

A Make columns and group the target vocabulary words by the number of syllables.

B Look up each target vocabulary word in a dictionary. Note any differences from the meanings in the Glossary.

WORD ROOT

Tell students that, in addition to its scientific meaning, *acid* is also used as an adjective to describe; for example, someone's sense of humor or style of writing. Challenge students to write a sentence using this figurative meaning of *acid*.

C Combine each pair of sentences into one sentence that provides the same information.

D Underline the subjects and circle the predicates in each sentence you wrote.

acid   soluble   alkaline   neutral   litmus paper
ion   base   pH   indicator   neutralize

C. Write the vocabulary word that best completes each pair of sentences.

1. An atom with an electric charge is an _____ion_____ .
   H^+ represents a hydrogen _____ion_____ in an acid.

2. A substance that dissolves in water is _____soluble_____ .
   Acids and bases are both _____soluble_____ substances.

3. The measure _____pH_____ tells how acidic or alkaline a solution is.
   A neutral solution has a _____pH_____ of 7.

4. Mixing an acid and a base will _____neutralize_____ them.
   Salt is a product of reactions that _____neutralize_____ acids and bases.

5. The presence of OH^- ions indicates a _____base_____ .
   A strong _____base_____ may have a pH of 13.

6. The presence of an acid is revealed by an _____indicator_____ .
   One common _____indicator_____ is litmus paper.

7. Acids turn blue _____litmus paper_____ red.
   Bases turn red _____litmus paper_____ blue.

8. A salt is a _____neutral_____ product of an acid-base reaction.
   A _____neutral_____ substance is not an acid or a base.

9. A substance that is a base is described as _____alkaline_____ .
   An _____alkaline_____ solution has hydroxide ions.

10. On the pH scale, the number 0 indicates a strong _____acid_____ .
    In water, an _____acid_____ gives up hydrogen ions.

32   Acids and Bases

---

acid   soluble   alkaline   neutral   litmus paper
ion   base   pH   indicator   neutralize

Students' answers will vary.

D. Use each pair of words in a sentence.

1. neutral, pH
   The pH of a neutral solution is 7.

2. indicator, base
   The color of an indicator changes to show if a solution
   is an acid or a base.

3. soluble, acid
   An acid is a substance that is soluble in water.

4. ion, neutralize
   In chemical reactions that neutralize an acid and a base,
   the OH^- ions and the H^+ ions join to form H_2O.

5. alkaline, litmus paper
   In an alkaline solution, red litmus paper turns blue.

Write!
Write your response to the prompt on a separate sheet of paper.
Use as many vocabulary words as you can in your writing.

You are given an acid and a base to combine. How will you know which
substance is which? How will the substances react when combined?

Acids and Bases   33

Write!

Distribute Writing Graphic Organizer: Idea Wheel,
Teacher Guide page 81. Tell students to write *Acids and
Bases* in the center of the wheel. Then on the spokes of
the wheel, they should write details about how they
will test the acid, how they will test the base, and how
the acid and base will react when combined.

Sample Answer

    *To find which solution is an acid and which is a base,
I would use the indicator called litmus paper. It would change
color. I would know that solution #1 is an acid formed from a
soluble substance that has given up hydrogen ions in the
solution. My solution #2 is alkaline. Testing the pH of each
solution, I find solution #1 is a 6, and solution #2 is an 8.*

    *If my chemistry teacher said it was safe to do,
I would mix the two solutions and see if they react. A
neutral salt and water are the products, so I know my
reaction did neutralize the acid and base.*

TAKE-HOME ACTIVITY

Assign the Take-Home Activity to students for
additional practice with the target vocabulary words.
The reproducible Take-Home Activity for Lesson 5
is on page 88 of the Teacher Guide.

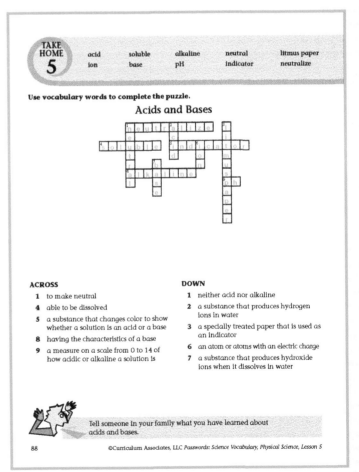

TAKE HOME 5

acid   soluble   alkaline   neutral   litmus paper
ion   base   pH   indicator   neutralize

Use vocabulary words to complete the puzzle.

Acids and Bases

ACROSS
1 to make neutral
4 able to be dissolved
5 a substance that changes color to show
  whether a solution is an acid or a base
8 having the characteristics of a base
9 a measure on a scale from 0 to 14 of
  how acidic or alkaline a solution is

DOWN
1 neither acid nor alkaline
2 a substance that produces hydrogen
  ions in water
3 a specially treated paper that is used as
  an indicator
6 an atom or atoms with an electric charge
7 a substance that produces hydroxide
  ions when it dissolves in water

Tell someone in your family what you have learned about
acids and bases.

88   ©Curriculum Associates, LLC *Passwords: Science Vocabulary, Physical Science, Lesson 5*

Acids and Bases   35

LESSON 6

Motion and Forces

(Student Book pages 34–39)

TARGET VOCABULARY

inertia the tendency of an object to resist change in motion

balanced forces forces acting on an object when it is at rest or moving at a constant speed in a constant direction

momentum a measure of an object's motion

velocity the speed and direction of an object

acceleration a change in velocity

unbalanced forces forces resulting in a change in velocity

net force the difference in strength and direction of all the forces acting on an object

friction a force that resists movement

action force the force acting on an object

reaction force the force opposing the action force

COGNATES

Spanish-speaking students may find a discussion of the similarities and differences between English and Spanish cognates helpful.

English	Spanish
inertia	inercia
velocity	velocidad
acceleration	aceleración
net force	fuerza neta
friction	fricción
reaction force	fuerza reacción

Lesson Summary When forces are balanced, inertia keeps an object at rest or in motion at the same speed and direction. An object's momentum is its mass times velocity, a measure based on both speed and direction. Unbalanced forces cause acceleration, or a change in velocity. The net force is the total difference in strength and direction of all the forces acting on an object. When an object exerts a force in one direction, the reaction forces push equally in the opposite direction.

BEFORE READING

Activate Prior Knowledge

Have students throw a ball gently into the air. Ask them why the ball goes up (*the force of their muscles*) and why it comes down (*gravity*). Have them roll a ball gently on the floor. Ask them why the ball goes forward (*again, the force of their muscles*) and why it slows down (*friction*).

Introduce Target Vocabulary

Tell students they are about to read a selection about motion and force. Write the target vocabulary words on the board. Model the pronunciation of each word and have student volunteers repeat the word. Discuss the meaning of each word and, if necessary, write the definition next to the word.

Present Graphic Organizer

Provide each student with a copy of Vocabulary Graphic Organizer: Four Square, Teacher Guide page 78. Have students choose or assign each student a different target vocabulary word. Have students write their word in the center. As they read the lesson, students should add information about the vocabulary word to the graphic organizer.

Word and Definition Cards
for Lesson 6 are on pages 109 and 110
of the Teacher Guide.

VOCABULARY STRATEGY: Compound Words

Review with students that a compound noun is made up of two words that express one idea. Ask students for examples of compound nouns and list them on the board (*boardwalk, fresh water, city-state, etc.*). Explain that compound nouns may be written in one of three ways: with a hyphen (a hyphenated compound), as a single word (a closed compound), or as two words written separately (an open compound). Point out examples from the list on the board or give students examples. Have students find the target vocabulary words that are compound nouns using *force* or *forces* (*balanced forces, unbalanced forces, reaction force, net force*). Lead them to see that used together, the two words of the compound have a single meaning.

Motion and Forces

LESSON 6

inertia momentum acceleration net force action force
balanced forces velocity unbalanced forces friction reaction force

If you throw a ball, what causes it to move? Why does it slow down and eventually hit the ground? Read this selection to explore how motion and force affect objects.

Motion and Forces

Inertia

Inertia is the tendency of an object to resist changes in motion. An object at rest will tend to stay at rest. An object in motion will tend to stay in motion in the same direction. When an object is at rest or moving at a constant speed in a constant direction, the forces acting on the object are **balanced forces**. If a new force is applied to the object, the force must overcome the inertia to create a change.

Describing Motion

Momentum is a measure of an object's motion. The formula for figuring out momentum is the mass of the object times its velocity. The **velocity** of an object includes both its speed and direction. If two objects with different masses are moving at the same velocity, the heavier object will have more momentum. For example, a golf ball rolling down a ramp has more momentum than a Ping-Pong ball. Likewise, if two baseballs have different velocities, the baseball with the greater velocity will also have greater momentum.

A change in velocity is **acceleration**. Since velocity includes both speed and direction, a change in either will change acceleration. An object speeding up has positive acceleration. An object slowing down has negative acceleration.

The Net Force

When the forces acting on an object are **unbalanced forces**, the velocity of the object changes. The **net force** is the total difference in strength and direction of all the forces acting on an object.

Suppose two groups of students are playing tug-of-war. One group pulls toward the right with greater force than the group pulling toward the left. The net force is found by subtracting the smaller force from the greater force. If each group pulled with an equal force in opposite directions, the forces would be balanced and the net force would be zero. The rope would not move.

In this game of tug-of-war, the forces are unbalanced. The difference between the two forces equals the net force.

The Forces of Gravity and Friction

Gravity is the force of attraction between objects. When you jump, your muscles exert an upward force. You land because the force of gravity between you and Earth is much stronger than the force of your jump.

Whenever two objects in contact move over each other, a force called **friction** opposes the movement. Friction causes objects to slow down. When you slide a box across the floor, you overcome friction.

Action and Reaction Forces

Forces work in pairs. Whenever one object exerts a force on another object, the second object exerts an equal force in the opposite direction. The force acting on an object is the **action force**. The equal and opposite force acting back is the **reaction force**.

When you hold a bow and draw back on an arrow in the bow string, the forces are balanced. You are pulling in one direction, and the bow is pulling just as hard in the other. When you release the arrow, the action force moves it forward. The reaction force, pushing equally hard, moves the bow backward.

Action and reaction forces are at work when an arrow is shot from a bow.

My Science Vocabulary
Go to page 95 to list other words you have learned about motion and force.

34   Motion and Forces

Motion and Forces   35

DURING READING

Read the selection aloud to students, stopping at the end of each paragraph or section. Review any words or concepts that students are having trouble with. Remind students that there is a glossary at the back of their book that contains all of the words that appear in boldfaced type in the lesson.

- Tell students that the root of *momentum* is *movere*, meaning "to move." The root of *inertia* is *iners*, which means "inert or idle." The root of *friction* is *fricare*, which mean "to rub." The root of *velocity* is *velox*, which means "fast." Ask how each word relates to the meaning of its root. (*Momentum is inertia of motion; inertia is to resist change, or remain idle if idle; friction results from rubbing; velocity includes speed and direction.*)

- Explain to students that the force of gravity is greater for objects with more mass and greater as objects are closer together. Explain that friction depends on the weight of the object being moved and the texture of the surface that is moved over.

Have students read the selection again on their own.

AFTER READING

Review Graphic Organizers

Answer any questions students have about the reading selection. Then have students complete or review their graphic organizer and share it with the class.

Summarize

Have students work together to come up with either a written or an oral summary of the lesson. Encourage students to use the target vocabulary words as the basis of their summary. Have students share their summary with the class.

My Science Vocabulary

Encourage students to turn to My Science Vocabulary on page 95 of the student book and use the space provided to add other words about motion and forces.

A. Match each word with its meaning. Write the letter of the correct meaning on the line in front of each word.

1. __c__ reaction force
2. __a__ friction
3. __f__ balanced forces
4. __j__ velocity
5. __e__ momentum
6. __h__ action force
7. __g__ inertia
8. __i__ unbalanced forces
9. __d__ net force
10. __b__ acceleration

a. the force that opposes movement when two objects are in contact with each another

b. a change in velocity

c. the force that pushes equally hard in the direction opposite the action force

d. the total difference in strength and direction of all the forces acting on an object

e. a measure of an object's motion

f. the forces acting on an object when it is at rest or moving at a constant speed in a constant direction

g. the tendency of an object at rest to remain at rest and an object in motion to stay in motion in the same direction

h. the force acting on an object that causes it to react

i. the forces acting on an object that cause its velocity to change

j. the speed and direction of an object

B. Circle the word that makes sense in each sentence. Then write the word.

1. When two objects move against each other, the force of (friction, acceleration) resists the movement. _____friction_____

2. An object has inertia because the forces acting on the object are (balanced forces, unbalanced forces). _____balanced forces_____

3. When you release an arrow from a bow, the (inertia, action force) moves the arrow forward. _____action force_____

4. When forces acting on an object are unbalanced, the (net force, friction) cannot be zero. _____net force_____

5. The product of an object's mass and velocity is its (gravity, momentum). _____momentum_____

6. The tendency of an object at rest to remain at rest is one example of (inertia, velocity). _____inertia_____

7. When one object pushes against another, the second object exerts an equal (friction, reaction force) that moves the first object in the opposite direction. _____reaction force_____

8. In a situation of (unbalanced forces, inertia), the velocity of an object changes. _____unbalanced forces_____

9. If the speed or direction of an object is changing, it has (acceleration, inertia). _____acceleration_____

10. The speed of an object and the direction it is traveling make up the object's (friction, velocity). _____velocity_____

ROOT

The word **inertia** comes from the Latin root **inertis**, which means "idle."

ACTIVITIES A–D

Encourage students to complete as many of the activities as possible. Remind students that they may refer to the Glossary at the back of their book as they complete the activities. Students may work independently, in small groups, or as a class. When students are done, discuss the answers for each activity.

Extensions

These extension ideas allow you to reuse or expand upon the activities. Share them with students who complete the activities before other students, or have students do them for additional practice with the target vocabulary words.

A Pick a target vocabulary word and write a description of an event, a situation, or an action that would help show someone else the meaning of the word.

B Renumber the sentences so that they are in alphabetical order by the target vocabulary words.

WORD ROOT

There is more than one comic book character who goes by the name Inertia. Based on their knowledge of the word and its root, have students suggest what a comic book character named Inertia might be like. Have students suggest what special abilities comic book superheroes and villains whose names are the other target vocabulary words might have.

C Choose one sentence and draw a picture, create a diagram, or write a formula to illustrate the sentence.

D Circle all the nouns and underline all the verbs in each of your sentences.

inertia	momentum	acceleration	net force	action force
balanced forces	velocity	unbalanced forces	friction	reaction force

C. *Choose the correct vocabulary word to complete each sentence.*

1. An object whose velocity increases has positive _____acceleration_____ .

2. The force that is equal to and opposite the action force is called the _____reaction force_____ .

3. A truck traveling at the same velocity as a motorcycle will have more _____momentum_____ because its mass is greater.

4. When a pair of sneakers and a wood floor are in contact, the force of _____friction_____ resists the motion of the sneakers.

5. A horse pulling on a wagon is an example of an _____action force_____ .

6. The velocity of an object changes when the forces acting on the object are _____unbalanced forces_____ .

7. An object's velocity is affected by the difference in the strength and direction of the forces, or the _____net force_____ , on the object.

8. If two objects have the same speed and mass and are moving in the same direction, they have the same _____velocity_____ .

9. A rolling ball will continue moving at the same speed in the same direction if _____balanced forces_____ are acting on it.

10. A book will lie still on a desk unless someone moves it because of _____inertia_____ .

38   *Motion and Forces*

Motion and Forces   39

inertia	momentum	acceleration	net force	action force
balanced forces	velocity	unbalanced forces	friction	reaction force

Students' answers will vary.

D. *Use each word in a sentence that shows you understand the meaning of the word.*

1. friction ___Two objects rubbing against each another experience friction.___

2. unbalanced forces ___An object will change speed or direction when unbalanced forces act on it.___

3. momentum ___An object's momentum is found by multiplying mass times velocity.___

4. action force ___The force that acts on an object is the action force.___

5. net force ___When one force and an opposite force have different strengths, the total difference is the net force.___

6. inertia ___A resting object experiences inertia and does not move until acted upon by a force.___

7. velocity ___The velocity of a car changes when the direction changes even if the speed stays the same.___

8. acceleration ___Acceleration is the change in the speed and direction of an object.___

9. balanced forces ___A bicycle traveling at a constant speed in the same direction is being acted upon by balanced forces.___

10. reaction force ___A reaction force is the force opposite to the action force.___

  Write!

Write your response to the prompt on a separate sheet of paper. Use as many vocabulary words as you can in your writing.

Describe the forces involved in the motion of something, such as a car, a bicycle, or a runner.

Write!

Distribute Writing Graphic Organizer: Sequence Chart, Teacher Guide page 83. In the first box, students should describe the motions and forces when their object first begins to move. In the following boxes, they should describe in order the motions and forces as the movement continues or changes.

Sample Answer

A bicycle at rest has inertia and balanced forces. Gravity keeps it on the ground. When a rider pedals the bike, the forces become unbalanced forces, and the rider's force overcomes the friction with the ground.

The action force of the foot pushing on the pedal has a reaction force of the pedal pushing on the foot. The velocity of the bicycle changes. The bike has positive acceleration because the net force of the rider's effort is greater than the forces opposing the motion. Then the rider stops pedaling, and momentum keeps the bicycle moving for a short time.

TAKE-HOME ACTIVITY

Assign the Take-Home Activity to students for additional practice with the target vocabulary words. The reproducible Take-Home Activity for Lesson 6 is on page 89 of the Teacher Guide.

Motion and Forces

TAKE HOME 6

inertia	momentum	acceleration	net force	action force
balanced forces	velocity	unbalanced forces	friction	reaction force

Use vocabulary words to complete the puzzle.

Motion and Forces

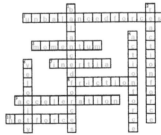

ACROSS

3. forces that cause a change in velocity
5. a measure of an object's motion
7. the tendency of an object to resist changes in motion
8. a force that opposes motion when two objects are in contact
9. a change in velocity
10. the difference in strength and direction of all the forces acting on an object

DOWN

1. the forces acting on an object when it is at rest
2. the force opposing the action force
4. the force acting on an object
6. the speed and direction of an object

Tell someone in your family what you have learned about motion and forces.

©Curriculum Associates, LLC *Passwords: Science Vocabulary, Physical Science, Lesson 6*   89

LESSON 7

Simple Machines

(Student Book pages 40–45)

Lesson Summary Work is the moving of an object in the direction of the effort force against the resistance force. Simple machines lessen the effort force. The higher the mechanical advantage, the higher the machine's efficiency. An inclined plane, or ramp, requires less effort because the distance is longer. A wedge is an inclined plane that moves. A screw is an inclined plane on a cylinder. A lever has a bar moving on a fixed point. A wheel and axle multiplies the effort force. A pulley changes the direction of the effort force.

TARGET VOCABULARY

effort force the force used to move an object

resistance force the force that opposes the effort force

mechanical advantage how much a machine adds to the effort force

efficiency the ratio of work done to effort used

inclined plane a ramp

wedge an inclined plane that moves

screw an inclined plane wrapped around a cylinder

lever a bar that moves on a fixed point

wheel and axle a larger wheel with a smaller axle

pulley a rope threaded around a wheel

COGNATES

Spanish-speaking students may find a discussion of the similarities and differences between English and Spanish cognates helpful.

English	Spanish
effort	esfuerzo
resistance force	fuerza resistencia
mechanical advantage	ventaja mecánica
efficiency	eficiencia
inclined plane	plano inclinado

BEFORE READING

Activate Prior Knowledge

Ask students to define the word *work*. Note their definitions on the board. Then explain that in science, *work* has a specific meaning. For example, doing homework may seem like work to students, but only moving the pencil to write words is "work." Holding a stack of books might seem like work, but in science, "work" is accomplished only when you move the books. Tell students this definition of work: Work is the movement of something over a distance in the direction of the force.

Introduce Target Vocabulary

Tell students they are about to read a selection about simple machines. Write the target vocabulary words on the board. Model the pronunciation of each word and have student volunteers repeat the word. Discuss the meaning of each word and, if necessary, write the definition next to the word.

Present Graphic Organizer

Provide each student with a copy of Vocabulary Graphic Organizer: Word Chart, Teacher Guide page 77. Assign each student a target vocabulary word. Have students fill in as much of the chart as they can. As they read the lesson, students should continue to add information to the chart.

Word and Definition Cards
for Lesson 7 are on pages 111 and 112
of the Teacher Guide.

VOCABULARY STRATEGY: Using Common Words

Tell students that sometimes to understand unknown words, such as science terms, they need to use their knowledge of common words. Point out the term *effort force*. From the word *effort*, they can guess that the term involves some kind of work. The word *force* means "strength or power." So, it makes sense that

effort force means "the power, or force, needed to move an object." Have students use the same approach to explain *resistance force (the power that resists work)* and *mechanical advantage (the benefit from a machine).*

Simple Machines

Simple Machines 41

LESSON 7

effort force   efficiency   screw   wheel and axle
resistance force   inclined plane   lever   pulley
mechanical advantage   wedge

When you have work to do, the right tools make it easier. How do tools help you do work? What exactly is work? Read this selection to learn about simple machines.

Simple Machines

What Work Is

For work to be done, an object must move, and a force must act on the object to make it move. The amount of work is the force times the distance.

> work = force x distance
> work = Fd
>
> *Work, in science, has a very specific meaning.*

Simple Machines

A simple machine is a device with few parts that makes work easier. It changes the strength or direction of the force a person applies to an object, so less force is needed to move the object.

The force used to move an object is the **effort force**. The force that opposes the effort force is the **resistance force**.

A simple machine provides a mechanical advantage. The **mechanical advantage** is the number of times the machine multiplies the effort force. If a machine doubles the person's effort force, the machine has a mechanical advantage of 2.

The **efficiency** of a machine measures how much work the machine does compared to the effort, or energy, used. An efficient machine has a higher mechanical advantage.

When you use an inclined plane, you cover more distance but exert less force.

Inclined Planes

One simple machine is an **inclined plane**, or ramp. It takes less force to push an object up a ramp than to pick it straight up, even if the object has to be moved a longer distance.

A **wedge** is an inclined plane that moves. It is often used to cut or push objects apart. An ax is a wedge. The thin edge of the ax overcomes the resistance force of a log to cut through it.

A **screw** is an inclined plane wrapped in a spiral around a cylinder. Like a nail, a screw can hold objects together. A screw must be moved over a longer distance than a nail, but less force is needed.

Levers

A **lever** is a bar that moves around a fixed point, or fulcrum. A crowbar is a type of lever. The object to be lifted is the load. The downward force applied to the crowbar is the effort force. The upward force the crowbar uses to lift the load is the resistance force.

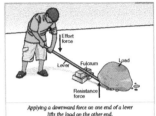
Applying a downward force on one end of a lever lifts the load on the other end.

Wheel and Axle

A **wheel and axle** is a simple machine made of a wheel with a rod, or axle, in the center. The effort force applied at the wheel is multiplied at the axle. The bigger the wheel is in comparison to the axle, the greater the mechanical advantage.

Pulleys

A **pulley** is a wheel with a rope or chain around it. A pulley helps with lifting heavy objects by changing the direction of the effort force from up to down.

> **My Science Vocabulary**
> Go to page 96 to list other words you have learned about simple machines.

DURING READING

Read the selection aloud to students, stopping at the end of each paragraph or section. Review any words or concepts that students are having trouble with. Remind students that there is a glossary at the back of their book that contains all of the words that appear in boldfaced type in the lesson.

- Discuss each type of simple machine and have students find additional examples of simple machines being used in the classroom, in pictures or illustrations, or in photos or diagrams on the Internet. Some examples include the following: ramp for the disabled (inclined plane); ax, nail (wedge); car jack (screw); balance, crowbar, scissors, tongs, seesaw, wheelbarrow (lever); doorknob, screwdriver, steering wheel (wheel and axle); window blinds, flagpole pulley, crane (pulley).

- Have students refer to the diagram of the lever on page 41. As a volunteer reads the labels, have students point to that part of the lever.

Have students read the selection again on their own.

AFTER READING

Review Graphic Organizers

Answer any questions students have about the reading selection. Then have students complete or review their graphic organizer and share it with the class.

Summarize

Have students work together to come up with either a written or an oral summary of the lesson. Encourage students to use the target vocabulary words as the basis of their summary. Have students share their summary with the class.

My Science Vocabulary

Encourage students to turn to My Science Vocabulary on page 96 of the student book and use the space provided to add other words about simple machines.

effort force	efficiency	screw	wheel and axle
resistance force	inclined plane	lever	pulley
mechanical advantage	wedge		

A. *Fill in the blanks with the correct vocabulary word.*

1. how much work a machine does compared to the energy used

   e f f i c i e n c y

2. an inclined plane that moves, such as an ax

   w e d g e

3. a bar that moves around a fixed point

   l e v e r

4. the force used to move an object

   e f f o r t   f o r c e

5. a ramp

   i n c l i n e d   p l a n e

6. a wheel with a rod attached to its center

   w h e e l   a n d   a x l e

7. the force that opposes the effort force

   r e s i s t a n c e   f o r c e

8. the number of times a machine multiplies the effort force

   m e c h a n i c a l   a d v a n t a g e

9. an inclined plane that wraps around a cylinder to form a spiral

   s c r e w

10. a wheel with a rope or a chain around it

    p u l l e y

---

effort force	efficiency	screw	wheel and axle
resistance force	inclined plane	lever	pulley
mechanical advantage	wedge		

B. *Choose and write the two words that best complete each sentence.*

| wheel and axle | pulley | inclined plane | screw |

1. A _____pulley_____ has a wheel with a rope or chain around it, while a _____wheel and axle_____ has a wheel with a rod through its center

| resistance force | lever | mechanical advantage | effort force |

2. The force used to move an object, or the _____effort force_____, is opposed by the _____resistance force_____.

| lever | mechanical advantage | inclined plane | effort force |

3. A ramp is an _____inclined plane_____, and a crowbar is a _____lever_____.

| efficiency | mechanical advantage | wedge | pulley |

4. A machine works with more _____efficiency_____ if it has a higher _____mechanical advantage_____.

| wheel and axle | screw | wedge | pulley |

5. An inclined plane that moves is a _____wedge_____, and an inclined plane wrapped around a cylinder is a _____screw_____.

ROOT

The word **mechanical** has its roots in the Greek word **mekhane**, which means "machine."

42   Simple Machines

Simple Machines   43

ACTIVITIES A–D

Encourage students to complete as many of the activities as possible. Remind students that they may refer to the Glossary at the back of their book as they complete the activities. Students may work independently, in small groups, or as a class. When students are done, discuss the answers for each activity.

Extensions

These extension ideas allow you to reuse or expand upon the activities. Share them with students who complete the activities before other students, or have students do them for additional practice with the target vocabulary words.

A Put the target vocabulary words in alphabetical order.

B Choose a sentence and draw a picture or diagram to illustrate its meaning.

C Rewrite each pair of sentences as a single sentence providing the same information.

D For each sentence you wrote, write a second sentence that provides details or examples related to your first sentence.

WORD ROOT

Have students list other English words that come from the Greek word *mekhane (machinery, machination, machinist, mechanic, mechanical, mechanize)*. Encourage students to add these words to the root words chart on page 99 of their book.

effort force   efficiency   screw   wheel and axle
resistance force   inclined plane   lever   pulley
mechanical advantage   wedge

C. *Write the vocabulary word that best completes each pair of sentences.*

1. The force used to move an object is the ___effort force___ .
   The ___effort force___ is opposed by the resistance force.

2. A ramp is an ___inclined plane___ .
   An ___inclined plane___ lessens effort but increases distance.

3. A wheel with a rope or chain around it makes a ___pulley___ .
   The direction of force can be changed by a ___pulley___ .

4. A simple machine has a ___mechanical advantage___ because
   it multiplies the effort force.
   A machine that doubles a person's effort force has a
   ___mechanical advantage___ of 2.

5. The force that opposes the effort force is the ___resistance force___ .
   The force a lever uses to lift a load is the ___resistance force___ .

6. An inclined plane that moves is a ___wedge___ .
   An ax is an example of a ___wedge___ .

7. A bar moving on a fixed point is a ___lever___ .
   A crowbar is one example of a ___lever___ .

8. The measure of how much work a machine does compared to the effort
   used is ___efficiency___ .
   A high mechanical advantage yields high ___efficiency___ .

9. An inclined plane around a cylinder is a ___screw___ .
   A ___screw___ spreads the effort along the spiral's length.

10. A wheel and rod make up a ___wheel and axle___ .
    A doorknob is an example of a ___wheel and axle___ .

44   *Simple Machines*

---

effort force   efficiency   screw   wheel and axle
resistance force   inclined plane   lever   pulley
mechanical advantage   wedge

Students' answers will vary.

D. *Use each word in a sentence that shows you understand the meaning of the word.*

1. wheel and axle ___A Ferris wheel is a giant wheel and axle.___

2. efficiency ___Is the efficiency of a power lawn mower greater than that
   of a push mower?___

3. effort force ___The force used to move an object is the effort force.___

4. wedge ___A wedge is an inclined plane that moves, such as an ax.___

5. pulley ___A pulley is used to raise the flag on a flagpole.___

6. mechanical advantage ___All simple machines provide a mechanical
   advantage.___

7. screw ___A screw makes use of a spiral inclined plane to spread
   the effort over a longer distance.___

8. resistance force ___The resistance force a crowbar uses pushes up on
   the load.___

9. efficiency ___The efficiency of a machine is a measure of how much
   work it can do for the effort put in.___

10. lever ___A bottle opener is one type of lever.___

 Write!

*Write your response to the prompt on a separate sheet of paper.
Use as many vocabulary words as you can in your writing.*

Imagine that your job is to evaluate simple machines. Write a description of some
simple machines that you would recommend and how you might rate them.

Simple Machines   45

Write!

Distribute Writing Graphic Organizer: Idea Wheel, Teacher Guide page 81. Tell students to write *Simple Machines* in the center of the wheel. Then on the spokes of the wheel, they should write details about each type of simple machine they will recommend and how they will evaluate these machines.

Sample Answer

I will recommend this inclined plane because the effort to push a box up the long ramp is less than lifting it. Over here, I have a pulley to lift heavy weights upward by pulling downward on the long rope. This ax is a wedge that cuts well. Over here, is a shovel, which is a lever. This screw requires little effort to go into wood. It has an inclined plane that wraps around its cylinder.

To evaluate the machines, I will find each machine's mechanical advantage. I am looking for the machines with the greatest efficiency.

TAKE-HOME ACTIVITY

Assign the Take-Home Activity to students for additional practice with the target vocabulary words. The reproducible Take-Home Activity for Lesson 7 is on page 90 of the Teacher Guide.

TAKE HOME 7

effort force   efficiency   screw   wheel and axle
resistance force   inclined plane   lever   pulley
mechanical advantage   wedge

Use vocabulary words to complete the puzzle.

Simple Machines

ACROSS

5. the number of times a machine multiplies the effort force
7. a measure of how much work a machine does compared to the effort used
9. a simple machine with a bar that moves around a fixed point
10. an inclined plane that moves

DOWN

1. a wheel with a rope or chain around it that changes the direction of the force
2. the force that opposes the effort force
3. a simple machine made of a wheel with a rod in the center
4. a ramp
6. the force used to move an object
8. an inclined plane wrapped in a spiral around a cylinder

Tell someone in your family what you have learned about simple machines.

90   ©Curriculum Associates, LLC *Passwords: Science Vocabulary, Physical Science, Lesson 7*

LESSON 8

Forms of Energy

(Student Book pages 46–51)

TARGET VOCABULARY

kinetic energy energy of action

potential energy stored energy

mechanical energy the total amount of potential and kinetic energy an object has

electrical energy energy of electrons

thermal energy heat energy

chemical energy energy given off by a chemical reaction

nuclear energy energy given off when atomic bonds are made or broken

radiant energy energy that moves in waves

energy transformation the changing of one form of energy to another

solar energy energy from the sun

COGNATES

Spanish-speaking students may find a discussion of the similarities and differences between English and Spanish cognates helpful.

English	Spanish
kinetic energy	energía cinética
potential energy	energía potencial
mechanical energy	energía mecánica
electrical energy	energía eléctrica
thermal energy	energía termal
chemical energy	energía química
nuclear energy	energía nuclear
radiant energy	energía radiante
energy transformation	transformación energía
solar energy	energía solar

VOCABULARY STRATEGY: Suffixes

Remind students that suffixes can be added to root words to create related adjectives. Have students note the nine target vocabulary words that are phrases that name types or forms of energy. Have students list the words from each of these target vocabulary words that have the following suffixes: *-ic (kinetic); -al (potential, mechanical, thermal, chemical, electrical); -ar (solar, nuclear); -ant (radiant).* Encourage students to add these words to the suffix chart on page 100 of their book.

Lesson Summary Energy can be kinetic or potential. Energy has different forms because it is produced by different sources. Mechanical energy is the energy of a moving object. Electrical energy is from the movement of electric charges. Thermal energy is heat. Chemical energy is produced by a chemical reaction. Nuclear energy comes from the breaking or fusing of atomic nuclei. Radiant energy moves in waves, such as solar energy from the sun. Energy can be transformed from one form to another, but not created or destroyed.

BEFORE READING

Activate Prior Knowledge

List on the board all the energy sources students may know of, such as a hydroelectric plant, cells in a plant, burning wood, the sun, and so on. Using items on the list, point out one or two examples that show how energy changes from one form to another, such as from solar energy to chemical energy in a plant, or from the mechanical energy of moving water to electricity to heat in a home.

Introduce Target Vocabulary

Tell students they are about to read a selection about forms of energy. Write the target vocabulary words on the board. Model the pronunciation of each word and have student volunteers repeat the word. Discuss the meaning of each word and, if necessary, write the definition next to the word.

Present Graphic Organizer

Provide each student with a copy of Vocabulary Graphic Organizer: Word Web, Teacher Guide page 76. Have students write *Energy Forms* in the center circle of the web. Have them write a target vocabulary word that names a form of energy in each outer circle. As they read the lesson, have students add definitions and information about the target vocabulary words in each circle. Tell them they may add circles, if necessary.

Word and Definition Cards
for Lesson 8 are on pages 113 and 114
of the Teacher Guide.

Forms of Energy

LESSON 8

kinetic energy electrical energy nuclear energy energy transformation
potential energy thermal energy radiant energy solar energy
mechanical energy chemical energy

How are gasoline, food, sunlight, and electricity alike? They all bring about changes or movement. They are all forms of energy. Read this selection to learn more about energy.

Forms of Energy

Kinetic and Potential Energy

Energy is the ability to do work or cause a change. There are many forms of energy. All forms fit into two main types: kinetic energy and potential energy. **Kinetic energy** is the energy produced by the motion of an object. A rolling ball or a moving bicycle has kinetic energy. **Potential energy** is the energy that is stored in an object. An object may have potential energy because of its position. A ball or bike resting at the top of a hill has potential energy. It has the potential to start moving.

Mechanical Energy

Objects can have both potential energy and kinetic energy. The total amount of potential energy and kinetic energy that an object has is called **mechanical energy**. A roller coaster, for example, has potential energy at the top of each hill. Each time the roller coaster moves downhill, it has kinetic energy. The coaster's energy keeps changing from kinetic to potential to kinetic, but the total mechanical energy stays the same.

A roller coaster's mechanical energy is a combination of its potential energy and kinetic energy.

Energy from Moving Electrons

The particles in matter have positive and negative charges. Electrons are the negatively charged particles. Their movement produces **electrical energy**. Lightning is a form of electrical energy. The wires in homes carry electrical energy to appliances.

Energy from Moving Molecules

The tiny particles, or molecules, that make up matter are always moving. The energy created by their movement is called **thermal energy**, or heat energy. The faster the molecules move, the greater the thermal energy.

Energy from Chemical Reactions

Chemical energy is energy stored in the bonds that hold molecules together. When there is a chemical reaction, the bonds break and chemical energy is released. Wood, for example, releases stored chemical energy when it is burned.

Energy from Atoms

Very strong forces hold together the nucleus, or center, of an atom. **Nuclear energy** is given off when the nucleus breaks apart or fuses with the nucleus of another atom. Nuclear energy is produced in nuclear power plants.

Radiant Energy

Radiant energy is energy that moves in waves, such as light from the sun. Radiant energy can move through matter, such as air or water, or through empty space. Radio waves are another example of radiant energy.

Conservation of Energy

Energy cannot be created or destroyed, but it can change from one form to another. This is called an **energy transformation**. For example, energy from the sun, or **solar energy**, travels as light, or radiant energy, to Earth. Green plants trap light energy and change it into chemical energy. When an animal eats the plant, the chemical energy is released.

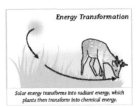

Energy Transformation

Solar energy transforms into radiant energy, which plants then transform into chemical energy.

My Science Vocabulary
Go to page 96 to list other words you have learned about forms of energy.

DURING READING

Read the selection aloud to students, stopping at the end of each paragraph or section. Review any words or concepts that students are having trouble with. Remind students that there is a glossary at the back of their book that contains all of the words that appear in boldfaced type in the lesson.

- Point out that *thermal* is based on the Greek word *thermos*, meaning "hot." Ask students for a word from the same root naming a device that measures heat *(thermometer)*; a device that regulates temperature in a building *(thermostat)*; and a container that keeps food hot *(thermos)*.

- Point out that nuclear energy comes from changes in the nucleus of an atom. The nucleus may lose particles or gain particles from another nucleus. Have students use a dictionary to find the plural of *nucleus (nuclei)*.

- Tell students that *solar* comes from *sol*, the Latin word for *sun*. Have students list other terms that contain the word *solar (solar battery, solar cell, solar day, solar flare, solar system, and so on).*

Have students read the selection again on their own.

AFTER READING

Review Graphic Organizers

Answer any questions students have about the reading selection. Then have students complete or review their graphic organizer and share it with the class.

Summarize

Have students work together to come up with either a written or an oral summary of the lesson. Encourage students to use the target vocabulary words as the basis of their summary. Have students share their summary with the class.

My Science Vocabulary

Encourage students to turn to My Science Vocabulary on page 96 of the student book and use the space provided to add other words about forms of energy.

kinetic energy   electrical energy   nuclear energy   energy transformation
potential energy   thermal energy   radiant energy   solar energy
mechanical energy chemical energy

A. Fill in the blanks with the correct vocabulary word.

1. energy that moves in waves through matter and empty space
   r a d i a n t   e n e r g y

2. the energy of motion
   k i n e t i c   e n e r g y

3. the changing of energy from one form to another
   e n e r g y   t r a n s f o r m a t i o n

4. energy given off when the nucleus of an atom breaks apart
   or fuses with another nucleus
   n u c l e a r   e n e r g y

5. energy from the sun
   s o l a r   e n e r g y

6. energy given off during a chemical reaction
   c h e m i c a l   e n e r g y

7. stored energy
   p o t e n t i a l   e n e r g y

8. energy produced by moving electrons
   e l e c t r i c a l   e n e r g y

9. energy produced by the movement of molecules
   t h e r m a l   e n e r g y

10. the total amount of potential energy and kinetic energy that an object has
    m e c h a n i c a l   e n e r g y

---

kinetic energy   electrical energy   nuclear energy   energy transformation
potential energy   thermal energy   radiant energy   solar energy
mechanical energy chemical energy

B. Circle the word that makes sense in each sentence. Then write the word.

1. The sun's energy is also called (solar energy, electrical energy).
   solar energy

2. A moving object has (potential energy, kinetic energy).
   kinetic energy

3. Appliances in homes run on (electrical energy, radiant energy).
   electrical energy

4. Another name for heat energy is (chemical energy, thermal energy).
   thermal energy

5. When one form of energy changes to another form,
   an (electrical energy, energy transformation) takes place.
   energy transformation

6. Potential energy that is released through a chemical reaction is
   (mechanical energy, chemical energy). chemical energy

7. The combined kinetic energy and potential energy of an object is
   (mechanical energy, thermal energy). mechanical energy

8. When the nucleus of an atom fuses with the nucleus of another atom,
   (radiant energy, nuclear energy) is released. nuclear energy

9. Stored energy is called (potential energy, mechanical energy).
   potential energy

10. Sunlight, which travels in waves through space, is (thermal energy,
    radiant energy). radiant energy

WORD ROOT
The word **kinetic** is based on the Greek word **kinein**, which means "to move."

ACTIVITIES A–D

Encourage students to complete as many of the activities as possible. Remind students that they may refer to the Glossary at the back of their book as they complete the activities. Students may work independently, in small groups, or as a class. When students are done, discuss the answers for each activity.

Extensions

These extension ideas allow you to reuse or expand upon the activities. Share them with students who complete the activities before other students, or have students do them for additional practice with the target vocabulary words.

A In any order, use the letters in the target vocabulary word *energy transformation* to make as many smaller words as you can, such as *go* and *tame*. Put a star next to each smaller word whose meaning relates to the target vocabulary word.

B Create an analogy using one or more of the target vocabulary words. Example: thermal energy : heat :: electrical energy : electricity

WORD ROOT

Ask students to relate the meaning of the word *kinein* to the target vocabulary word *kinetic energy*. (*Kinetic energy is the energy produced by the movement of an object.*) Explain that anything that is moving has kinetic energy, which can be produced by any of the forms of energy.

C Choose one sentence and draw a picture or diagram to illustrate the sentence. Add a title to your illustration.

D Write the target vocabulary words in groups that are related in some way. Groups may have one or more words.

kinetic energy electrical energy nuclear energy energy transformation
potential energy thermal energy radiant energy solar energy
mechanical energy chemical energy

C. *Choose the correct vocabulary word to complete each sentence.*

1. The motion of a rolling ball is _____kinetic energy_____ .

2. Burning wood causes a chemical reaction that releases
_____chemical energy_____ .

3. Lightning is a form of _____electrical energy_____ .

4. When an electric stove changes electrical energy into thermal energy,
an _____energy transformation_____ occurs.

5. Light, radio waves, and other waves that travel through matter
are all forms of _____radiant energy_____ .

6. The faster molecules of matter move, the more _____thermal energy_____
there is.

7. A baseball that is about to be thrown has _____potential energy_____ .

8. Another name for energy from the sun is _____solar energy_____ .

9. When the nucleus of an atom breaks apart _____nuclear energy_____
is produced.

10. You can add an object's kinetic and potential energy together to find its
_____mechanical energy_____ .

---

kinetic energy electrical energy nuclear energy energy transformation
potential energy thermal energy radiant energy solar energy
mechanical energy chemical energy

Students' answers will vary.

D. *Use each pair of words in a sentence.*

1. nuclear energy, solar energy
Would you rather your home be heated by nuclear energy
or solar energy?

2. potential energy, kinetic energy
A skateboard has potential energy when it is sitting at the top of a ramp
and kinetic energy when it is moving down the ramp.

3. electrical energy, mechanical energy
Electrical energy can make an appliance like a fan operate,
and thereby produce mechanical energy.

4. radiant energy, thermal energy
When radiant energy reaches Earth it can create thermal, or heat energy.

5. chemical energy, energy transformation
In one kind of energy transformation, green plants trap radiant energy
and change it into chemical energy.

 Write!
Write your response to the prompt on a separate sheet of paper.
Use as many vocabulary words as you can in your writing.

Suppose that you could be pure energy, moving from one form to another.
Describe a series of steps you might take to change form and learn about yourself.

Write!

Distribute Writing Graphic Organizer: Narrative Map, Teacher Guide page 82. Have students work with a partner or in a small group to brainstorm ideas for writing. Students can create a character, or they can be the main character. Setting(s) should include where the steps occur. Main events should include what occurs.

Sample Answer

I begin as potential energy in an electric circuit. When the switch is turned, I become electrical energy flowing into appliances. I am now kinetic energy! The fruit in the blender has chemical energy. Next, in a toaster, I transform into thermal energy. I go into a light bulb and become the type of radiant energy we recognize as light.

I see a collector for solar energy on the roof. I go back to the sun, where solar energy is produced.

TAKE-HOME ACTIVITY

Assign the Take-Home Activity to students for additional practice with the target vocabulary words. The reproducible Take-Home Activity for Lesson 8 is on page 91 of the Teacher Guide.

TAKE HOME 8

kinetic energy electrical energy nuclear energy energy transformation
potential energy thermal energy radiant energy solar energy
mechanical energy chemical energy

Use vocabulary words to complete the puzzle.

Forms of Energy

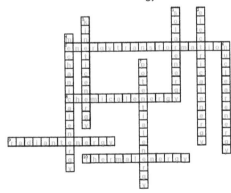

ACROSS

5 the change of one form of energy to another
8 energy released from a chemical reaction
9 energy that moves in waves
10 heat energy

DOWN

1 radiant energy from the sun

2 energy produced by the movement of electrons
3 energy produced by the motion of an object
4 the total amount of potential and kinetic energy an object has
6 energy given off when the nucleus of an atom breaks apart
7 stored energy

 Tell someone in your family what you have learned about forms of energy.

©Curriculum Associates, LLC *Passwords: Science Vocabulary, Physical Science, Lesson 8*   91

LESSON 9
The Properties of Waves

(Student Book pages 52–57)

Lesson Summary A transverse wave moves up and down, at right angles to the direction of movement of the energy. A longitudinal wave moves forward and back, in the same direction. A transverse wave has crests and troughs. The distance between crests on two succeeding waves is the wavelength. The amplitude is the depth of the wave, or its height from a midline. The frequency is how many waves pass a point in a given time. Waves may reflect back, or they refract due to a change of speed when moving into a new medium.

TARGET VOCABULARY

wave a disturbance that transfers energy

transverse wave a wave that moves up and down

longitudinal wave a wave that moves back and forth

crest the top of a transverse wave

trough the bottom of a transverse wave

wavelength the distance from crest to crest

amplitude the depth or height of a wave

frequency the number of waves in a given time

reflection the bouncing back of a wave

refraction the bending of a wave

COGNATES

Spanish-speaking students may find a discussion of the similarities and differences between English and Spanish cognates helpful.

English	Spanish
longitudinal	longitudinal
crest	cresta
amplitude	amplitud
frequency	frecuencia
reflection	reflejo
refraction	refracción

BEFORE READING

Activate Prior Knowledge

Bring in or have students bring in a Slinky. (If a Slinky is not available, you can model the transverse waves as described below with a piece of string or rope.) With the Slinky, demonstrate transverse waves that move the Slinky up and down, like ocean waves. Then demonstrate the movement of longitudinal waves by having someone hold one end steady while you push and pull the Slinky supported by a tabletop. Have students read the paragraph above the title of the lesson. Ask students which type of wave is represented by a pebble in water *(transverse wave)*.

Introduce Target Vocabulary

Tell students they are about to read a selection about the properties of waves. Write the target vocabulary words on the board. Model the pronunciation of each word and have student volunteers repeat the word. Discuss the meaning of each word and, if necessary, write the definition next to the word.

Present Graphic Organizer

Provide each student with a copy of Vocabulary Graphic Organizer: Word Chart, Teacher Guide page 77. Have half the students write *transverse wave* and half write *longitudinal wave* in the Word box. Have students fill in as much of the chart as they can. As they read the lesson, students should continue to add information to the chart.

Word and Definition Cards
for Lesson 9 are on pages 115 and 116
of the Teacher Guide.

VOCABULARY STRATEGY: Multimeaning Words

Several of the target vocabulary words have more than one meaning. Remind students that context clues can help them determine which meaning of the word should be applied. Ask students what different things the word *wave* can refer to *(ocean wave, hand wave, curl in hair, heat wave, a group of people)*. Encourage students to list or find in the dictionary different meanings of the following target vocabulary words: *crest (tuft on a bird, design on a helmet, heraldry, top of a hill)* and *trough (gutter, drinking bowl, low point)*.

The Properties of Waves

wave   longitudinal wave   trough   amplitude   reflection
transverse wave   crest   wavelength   frequency   refraction

Suppose you throw a pebble into still water. Circles of waves move out from the pebble. What are these circles? Read this selection to see if you guessed correctly.

The Properties of Waves

A **wave** is a disturbance that transfers energy through matter, such as air or water, or through space. A wave moves in a regular, repeating pattern.

Some waves, such as water waves, move the matter they pass through up and down, at right angles to the direction the waves are moving. This type of wave is called a **transverse wave**.

Another type of wave is a **longitudinal wave**. When longitudinal waves move through matter, the matter moves backward and forward in the same direction that the wave is moving. Sound waves are longitudinal waves.

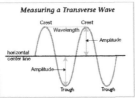

Transverse Waves — Direction of wave motion

Longitudinal Waves — Direction of wave motion

Measuring Wavelength

Transverse waves have repeating high points and low points, creating the wave pattern. Each high point, or top, of a wave is called a **crest**. The low point, or bottom, of a wave is a **trough**. The distance between the crest of one wave and the crest of the next wave is called the **wavelength**.

Amplitude and Frequency

The distance between the crest or trough and the horizontal line through the wave's center is the **amplitude** of the wave. Amplitude is a measure of how much the wave moves matter up and down from its resting position. It is the height or depth of the wave.

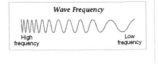

Measuring a Transverse Wave

Crest   Crest
Wavelength
Amplitude
horizontal center line
Amplitude
Trough   Trough

A third characteristic of waves is **frequency**. Frequency is the number of waves that pass a certain point in a given amount of time. Waves with a high frequency are close together; that is, the distance between crests is short. Low frequency means waves are far apart.

Wave Frequency
High frequency — Low frequency

Behavior of Waves

When a wave hits something, it may bounce off, just as a light wave does in a mirror. **Reflection** is the bouncing back of a wave that hits a surface. The speed of the wave does not change, but its direction does.

Reflection changes the direction of a wave.

When a wave moves from one type of matter to another, it goes slower or faster. The change in the wave's speed causes refraction. **Refraction** is the bending of a wave. For example, light waves slow down and bend as they pass from air into water. The refraction of the light waves causes objects in the water to appear bent too.

Refraction occurs because of a change in speed as light waves move from air into water.

My Science Vocabulary
Go to page 96 to list other words you have learned about the properties of waves.

DURING READING

Read the selection aloud to students, stopping at the end of each paragraph or section. Review any words or concepts that students are having trouble with. Remind students that there is a glossary at the back of their book that contains all of the words that appear in boldfaced type in the lesson.

- Explain to students that since longitudinal waves do not have the common wave shape associated with transverse waves, they do not have literal high points, or crests, and low points, or troughs. However, a longitudinal wave has places where particles are pushed together, called compressions, and where particles are spread apart, called refractions.

- Have students find the two target vocabulary words with the prefix *re-* (reflection, refraction). Tell students that *re-* is a Latin prefix that can mean "back, or away." *Reflection* combines *re-* with *flectere*, meaning "to flex or bend"; together it means "to bend back." *Refraction* combines *re-* with *frangere*, meaning "to break"; together it means "to break away or apart" from its previous path.

- Have students review the pictures of reflection and refraction on page 53. Have students trace with a finger the path of the light wave in reflection (straight into the mirror and straight back) and in refraction (straight from the source and then bending when it enters water).

Have students read the selection again on their own.

AFTER READING

Review Graphic Organizers

Answer any questions students have about the reading selection. Then have students complete or review their graphic organizer and share it with the class.

Summarize

Have students work together to come up with either a written or an oral summary of the lesson. Encourage students to use the target vocabulary words as the basis of their summary. Have students share their summary with the class.

My Science Vocabulary

Encourage students to turn to My Science Vocabulary on page 96 of the student book and use the space provided to add other words about the properties of waves.

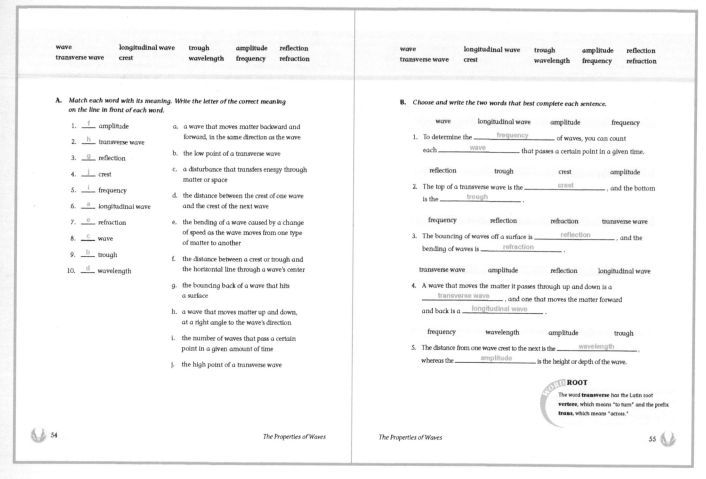

ACTIVITIES A–D

Encourage students to complete as many of the activities as possible. Remind students that they may refer to the Glossary at the back of their book as they complete the activities. Students may work independently, in small groups, or as a class. When students are done, discuss the answers for each activity.

Extensions

These extension ideas allow you to reuse or expand upon the activities. Share them with students who complete the activities before other students, or have students do them for additional practice with the target vocabulary words.

A Put the target vocabulary words in alphabetical order.

B Draw a picture or diagram for which one of the sentences would be an appropriate caption.

WORD ROOT

Have students explain how the meaning of the root *vertere* relates to the meaning of *transverse wave (it is a wave that is turned across at an angle to the direction of movement)*. Then tell students that *longitudinal* means "moving lengthwise, or running lengthwise." Ask students for the common geography term that has the same root as *longitudinal (longitude)*.

C Circle the simple subject (main noun) and underline the simple predicate (main verb) in each sentence. Look for four sentences that have more than one subject-verb pair.

D Rewrite each of your sentences so that the target vocabulary words appear in the opposite order.

C. *Write the vocabulary word that best completes each pair of sentences.*

1. Sound waves are one kind of _____longitudinal wave_____ .
   A _____longitudinal wave_____ moves matter forward and backward.

2. The top of a transverse wave is a _____crest_____ .
   The high point of a wave is called the _____crest_____ .

3. The measure of how much the wave moves matter up and down is _____amplitude_____ .
   The height or depth of a wave is _____amplitude_____ .

4. The bouncing back of a wave is _____reflection_____ .
   When a light wave hits a mirror, _____reflection_____ takes place.

5. The distance from crest to crest is the _____wavelength_____ .
   High-frequency waves have a short _____wavelength_____ .

6. When waves change speed, _____refraction_____ occurs.
   Moving from air to water causes the _____refraction_____ of light waves.

7. A water wave is an example of a _____transverse wave_____ .
   A _____transverse wave_____ moves the matter it passes through up and down.

8. The number of waves per unit of time is _____frequency_____ .
   Waves with low _____frequency_____ are far apart.

9. The bottom of a transverse wave is a _____trough_____ .
   The _____trough_____ is the lowest point on the wave.

10. A disturbance that moves energy is a _____wave_____ .
    A _____wave_____ moves in a regular, repeating pattern.

 56   *The Properties of Waves*

Students' answers will vary.

D. *Use each pair of words in a sentence.*

1. trough, amplitude
   The amplitude of a transverse wave can be measured from
   the center line of the wave to the trough.

2. wavelength, frequency
   The lower the frequency of waves, the longer their wavelength is.

3. crest, transverse wave
   Every transverse wave has a crest and a trough.

4. wave, longitudinal wave
   A longitudinal wave moves the matter it passes through in the same
   direction the wave is moving.

5. reflection, refraction
   When a wave bounces off a surface, reflection occurs, but when
   it moves through a surface into different matter and changes speed,
   refraction occurs.

Write!
Write your response to the prompt on a separate sheet of paper.
Use as many vocabulary words as you can in your writing.

Suppose you are listening to music at a beach with waves you can see. Describe
the kinds of waves you see and hear. What happens as you watch and listen?

The Properties of Waves   57

Write!

Distribute Writing Graphic Organizer: Idea Wheel, Teacher Guide page 81. Tell students to write *Waves* in the center of the wheel. Then on the spokes of the wheel, they should write details about the kinds of waves they are seeing and the kinds they are hearing.

Sample Answer

  I am watching a water wave, which is a transverse wave. The amplitude of this wave is about 5 feet. I know this because it dips down that far from the normal surface of the water. The frequency of the water wave is about 40 waves per minute. The wavelength, from the crest to the crest of the next wave, is about 10 feet. When I step in the water, my legs look as if they bend because of refraction. Light changes speed in the water.

  I am also listening to sound, which is a longitudinal wave. The reflection of this sound off a rock wall makes it seem as if the sound is coming from the wall.

TAKE-HOME ACTIVITY

Assign the Take-Home Activity to students for additional practice with the target vocabulary words. The reproducible Take-Home Activity for Lesson 9 is on page 92 of the Teacher Guide.

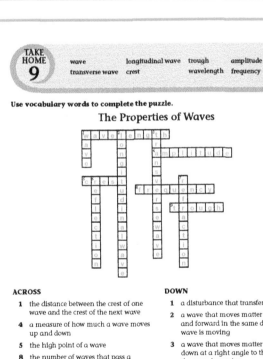

TAKE HOME 9

wave   longitudinal wave   trough   amplitude   reflection
transverse wave   crest   wavelength   frequency   refraction

Use vocabulary words to complete the puzzle.

The Properties of Waves

ACROSS

1 the distance between the crest of one wave and the crest of the next wave
4 a measure of how much a wave moves up and down
5 the high point of a wave
8 the number of waves that pass a certain point in a given time
9 the lowest point of a wave

DOWN

1 a disturbance that transfers energy
2 a wave that moves matter backward and forward in the same direction the wave is moving
3 a wave that moves matter up and down at a right angle to the direction the wave is moving
6 the bouncing back of a wave
7 the bending of a wave caused by a change of speed as the wave moves from one type of matter to another

Tell someone in your family what you have learned about the properties of waves.

The Properties of Waves   51

LESSON 10

Heat

(Student Book pages 58–63)

TARGET VOCABULARY

heat transfer the movement of heat from matter with a higher temperature to matter with a lower temperature

conduction the heat transfer caused by direct contact

convection the heat transfer by currents in a fluid

radiation the heat transfer by energy waves

expansion an increase in volume caused by heating

contraction a decrease in volume caused by cooling

Fahrenheit scale the temperature scale with 32° as the freezing point of water

Celsius scale the temperature scale with 0° as the freezing point of water

Kelvin scale the temperature scale with 0 as the temperature when kinetic energy is zero

calorie the energy needed to raise one gram of water 1°C

COGNATES

Spanish-speaking students may find a discussion of the similarities and differences between English and Spanish cognates helpful.

English	Spanish
transfer	transferencia
conduction	conducción
convection	convección
radiation	radiación
expansion	expansión
contraction	contracción
calorie	caloría

VOCABULARY STRATEGY: Proper Nouns

Point out that sometimes words in science are proper nouns that name the scientist who created or discovered something. Ask students to list the target vocabulary words that contain proper nouns (*Fahrenheit scale, Celsius scale, Kelvin scale*). Have students research the origin of these proper nouns.

Lesson Summary Heat is the energy of movement of particles of matter. Matter expands when heated and contracts when cooled. Heat is transferred by conduction when objects are touching. Heat is transferred by convection currents in unevenly heated fluids. Radiation is the transfer of heat by energy waves. The Fahrenheit and the Celsius scales are based on the freezing point of water. The Kelvin scale uses 0 for the point at which matter has no kinetic energy. Heat is the total energy of matter and can be measured in calories.

BEFORE READING

Activate Prior Knowledge

Have students read the temperature in Fahrenheit and in Celsius from a thermometer. Ask them why the numbers are different (*because the scales use a different base*). Ask if a degree Fahrenheit is the same as a degree Celsius. Help students understand that on the Fahrenheit scale, there are 180° between the freezing and the boiling point of water; on the Celsius scale, there are 100°. Therefore, 1.0 degrees Celsius equals 1.8 degrees Fahrenheit.

Introduce Target Vocabulary

Tell students they are about to read a selection about heat. Write the target vocabulary words on the board. Model the pronunciation of each word and have student volunteers repeat the word. Discuss the meaning of each word and, if necessary, write the definition next to the word.

Present Graphic Organizer

Provide each student with a copy of Vocabulary Graphic Organizer: Word Web, Teacher Guide page 76. Have students write *Heat* in the center circle of the web. As they read the lesson, have students group related target vocabulary words in the outer circles. Have them write a phrase next to each circle that explains why they grouped the words together.

Word and Definition Cards
for Lesson 10 are on pages 117 and 118
of the Teacher Guide.

(Gabriel Daniel Fahrenheit, 1686–1736, was a German physicist who developed the mercury thermometer. Anders Celsius, 1701–1774, was a Swedish astronomer who created the Celsius scale. William Thomson, First Baron of Kelvin, 1824–1907, was the British physicist, mathematician, and inventor responsible for the Kelvin scale.)

Heat

LESSON 10

heat transfer   convection   expansion   Fahrenheit scale   Kelvin scale
conduction   radiation   contraction   Celsius scale   calorie

If you are cold, a heated room makes you feel warm. How does the heat from the room warm you up? What exactly is heat? How is heat measured? Read this selection to learn about heat.

Heat

What Heat Is

The tiny particles, or molecules, in matter are constantly moving. Their movement produces a form of energy called thermal energy. Heat is the flow of thermal energy from one thing to another.

Heat always moves from matter with a higher temperature to matter with a lower temperature. **Heat transfer** from one type of matter to another occurs in three ways.

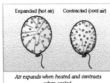

Expanded (hot air)   Contracted (cool air)

Air expands when heated and contracts when cooled.

Conduction

Conduction is the transfer of heat that happens when molecules of matter have direct contact. Faster-moving molecules in the hotter matter bump into slow-moving molecules in the cooler matter and transfer energy to them. Over time, all the molecules will move at the same speed with the same amount of energy, so their temperature will be the same.

Convection

Convection is the transfer of heat that happens when molecules of matter move from one place to another, carrying energy with them. Convection occurs in unevenly heated fluids. The hotter fluid near the heat source expands and rises, while the cooler fluid sinks to take its place and is heated. The up-and-down current continues to move heat through the fluid until the temperature is the same throughout.

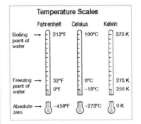

Heat transfers by conduction between the hot sand and the water, by convection currents in air, and by radiation from the sun.

Radiation

Radiation is the transfer of heat in the form of energy waves. Radiation can carry heat energy through empty space to another object. The sun's heat travels by radiation and warms Earth.

Expansion and Contraction

Matter increases in volume, or fills up more space, when it gains heat. This **expansion** happens because heat causes the molecules to move faster and push farther apart. When matter cools, the molecules lose energy, move more slowly, and come closer together. This **contraction** decreases the volume of matter.

Measuring Temperature and Heat

Temperature is a measure of how much movement energy, or kinetic energy, molecules of matter have. There are three main temperature scales. Two are based on water and use degrees as the units. On the **Fahrenheit scale**, water freezes at 32°F and boils at 212°F. On the **Celsius scale**, water freezes at 0°C and boils at 100°C.

Temperature Scales

	Fahrenheit	Celsius	Kelvin
Boiling point of water	212°F	100°C	373 K
Freezing point of water	32°F / 0°F	0°C / –18°C	273 K / 255 K
Absolute zero	–459°F	–273°C	0 K

The third scale uses a unit of measure called the kelvin (K), which is equal to one degree Celsius. The **Kelvin scale** is based on the temperature at which the molecules have no kinetic energy, or 0 K. On the Kelvin scale, water freezes at 273 K and boils at 373 K.

One unit used to measure heat is a calorie. A **calorie** is the amount of energy needed to raise the temperature of one gram of water one degree Celsius.

My Science Vocabulary

Go to page 97 to list other words you have learned about heat.

DURING READING

Read the selection aloud to students, stopping at the end of each paragraph or section. Review any words or concepts that students are having trouble with. Remind students that there is a glossary at the back of their book that contains all of the words that appear in boldfaced type in the lesson.

- Point out the target vocabulary word *heat transfer*. Explain to students that *transfer* uses the Latin prefix *trans-*, which means "across," and the root *ferre*, which means "to carry." A heat transfer carries heat across from one thing to another. Ask students to list other words that use the prefix *trans-* (*transmit, transit, transform, transistor, translate*, and so on). Encourage students to add these words to the prefix chart on page 100 of their book.

- Tell students that heat makes the molecules of matter vibrate faster and move farther away from each other. This movement causes expansion. Cooling slows down the movement of molecules and results in contraction.

- Tell students that *calorie* is from the Latin root *calor*, which means "heat." Point out that the calories represented by the target vocabulary word are different from Calories, with a capital C, listed on foods they eat. A food Calorie is equal to 1,000 calories, or one kilocalorie.

Have students read the selection again on their own.

AFTER READING

Review Graphic Organizers

Answer any questions students have about the reading selection. Then have students complete or review their graphic organizer and share it with the class.

Summarize

Have students work together to come up with either a written or an oral summary of the lesson. Encourage students to use the target vocabulary words as the basis of their summary. Have students share their summary with the class.

My Science Vocabulary

Encourage students to turn to My Science Vocabulary on page 97 of the student book and use the space provided to add other words about heat.

heat transfer   convection   expansion   **Fahrenheit scale**   **Kelvin scale**
conduction   radiation   contraction   **Celsius scale**   calorie

A. *Fill in the blanks with the correct vocabulary word.*

1. a decrease in volume caused by cooling
   c o n t r a c t i o n

2. the movement of heat from one type of matter to another
   h e a t   t r a n s f e r

3. a temperature scale on which water freezes at 32° and boils at 212°
   F a h r e n h e i t   s c a l e

4. the transfer of heat that happens when molecules of matter have direct contact
   c o n d u c t i o n

5. a temperature scale on which water freezes at 0° and boils at 100°
   C e l s i u s   s c a l e

6. the transfer of heat in the form of energy waves
   r a d i a t i o n

7. an increase in volume caused by heating
   e x p a n s i o n

8. a temperature scale based on the temperature at which the kinetic energy of molecules is zero
   K e l v i n   s c a l e

9. the amount of energy needed to raise the temperature of one gram of water one degree Celsius
   c a l o r i e

10. the transfer of heat that happens when molecules of matter move from one place to another
    c o n v e c t i o n

heat transfer   convection   expansion   **Fahrenheit scale**   **Kelvin scale**
conduction   radiation   contraction   **Celsius scale**   calorie

B. *Choose and write the two words that best complete each sentence.*

calorie   Celsius scale   Kelvin scale   radiation

1. The unit known as the _____calorie_____ is the amount of energy needed to raise one gram of water one degree on the _____Celsius scale_____ .

Fahrenheit scale   convection   Kelvin scale   expansion

2. Unlike the _____Fahrenheit scale_____ , which is based on how water behaves, the _____Kelvin scale_____ is based on the temperature at which molecules have no kinetic energy.

convection   expansion   contraction   conduction

3. When matter is heated, _____expansion_____ occurs, but _____contraction_____ occurs when matter is cooled.

radiation   heat transfer   conduction   calorie

4. In the process of _____heat transfer_____ by _____radiation_____ , heat moves through empty space from one object to another.

convection   contraction   Celsius scale   conduction

5. When two objects are touching, _____conduction_____ can transfer heat, and when a fluid is heated unevenly, _____convection_____ can transfer heat.

WORD ROOT

The word **convection** is based on the Latin word **convehere**, which means "to carry together or bring along."

ACTIVITIES A–D

Encourage students to complete as many of the activities as possible. Remind students that they may refer to the Glossary at the back of their book as they complete the activities. Students may work independently, in small groups, or as a class. When students are done, discuss the answers for each activity.

Extensions

These extension ideas allow you to reuse or expand upon the activities. Share them with students who complete the activities before other students, or have students do them for additional practice with the target vocabulary words.

A Make a word search puzzle with the target vocabulary words. Exchange puzzles with a classmate and see who can find all the words first.

B Go to the Internet and find a photo or illustration for each target vocabulary word.

WORD ROOT

Explain that the word *convehere*, comes from two simpler Latin word parts: *com (con)*, which means "together" and *vehere*, which means "to carry." Ask students to explain how the meanings of the Latin word parts relate to the meaning of *convection*. *(Heat is carried throughout the fluid, or brought along together in a current until the temperature is equalized.)* Note that *conduction* has the prefix *con-* with the root *ducere*, which means "to lead." In conduction, heat is led away from one object to another.

C Circle all the capitalized words in the sentences. Write rules to explain the capitalization of the words you circled.

D Circle each preposition you used in your sentences. Underline the prepositional phrases. Some of the prepositions you may have used include *in, of, by, from, with,* and *for.*

heat transfer   convection   expansion   **Fahrenheit scale**   **Kelvin scale**
conduction   radiation   contraction   **Celsius scale**   calorie

C. *Choose the correct vocabulary word to complete each sentence.*

1. The unit of measure for heat, the _____ calorie _____ , is based on the amount of energy needed to raise one gram of water one degree Celsius.

2. Water freezes at 0° and boils at 100° on the _____ Celsius scale _____ .

3. The temperature scale that does not use degrees is the _____ Kelvin scale _____ .

4. The sun's heat travels through empty space to Earth by _____ radiation _____ .

5. An increase in the volume of matter when it is heated is called _____ expansion _____ .

6. When two objects are in contact, the hotter object will transfer heat to the cooler object by _____ conduction _____ .

7. Water freezes at 32° and boils at 212° on the _____ Fahrenheit scale _____ .

8. Soup heated on a stove burner will become the same temperature throughout because a current called _____ convection _____ transfers the heat.

9. A decrease in the volume of matter when it is cooled is called _____ contraction _____ .

10. When temperature differences exist between different kinds of matter, _____ heat transfer _____ may take place by one of three methods.

62   *Heat*

---

heat transfer   convection   expansion   **Fahrenheit scale**   **Kelvin scale**
conduction   radiation   contraction   **Celsius scale**   calorie

Students' answers will vary.

D. *Use each word in a sentence that shows you understand the meaning of the word.*

1. contraction   The contraction of peas can occur when they are frozen.

2. Fahrenheit scale   The Fahrenheit scale uses 32° as the temperature at which water freezes.

3. convection   In fluids, heat transfers by convection.

4. calorie   A calorie is a measure of heat.

5. Kelvin scale   On the Kelvin scale, 0 K is the temperature at which molecules stop moving.

6. radiation   Radiation occurs when energy waves transfer heat.

7. expansion   Expansion of a balloon occurs when it is heated.

8. heat transfer   Heat transfer from hotter matter to cooler matter occurs in three different ways.

9. conduction   Molecules of matter have to be touching for conduction to take place because the particles bump into one another.

10. Celsius scale   Water freezes at 0° on the Celsius scale and boils at 100°.

 Write!
Write your response to the prompt on a separate sheet of paper.
Use as many vocabulary words as you can in your writing.

Write a description of heat energy you would enjoy experiencing and heat energy you do not want to experience.

Heat   63

Write!

Distribute Writing Graphic Organizer: Main Idea and Details Chart, Teacher Guide page 80. Tell students to write a main idea about heat energy they would enjoy in the first Main Idea box. Have them write a main idea about heat energy they would not enjoy in the second Main Idea box. Have them write details to support their main ideas in the corresponding Details boxes.

Sample Answer

    Outside in the hot sun, radiation from the sun is warming me. I enjoy this heat transfer. The temperature is about 85° on the Fahrenheit scale. A pleasant wind is blowing, perhaps from convection currents as the ground gets heated and the heated air rises.

    The metal chair I am sitting on is getting hot from the conduction of heat. I do not enjoy this. I'm glad it's not 0° on the Celsius scale though, or worse yet, 0 K on the Kelvin scale! I'd need millions of calories to warm me up from that!

TAKE-HOME ACTIVITY

Assign the Take-Home Activity to students for additional practice with the target vocabulary words. The reproducible Take-Home Activity for Lesson 10 is on page 93 of the Teacher Guide.

TAKE HOME 10

heat transfer   convection   expansion   **Fahrenheit scale**   **Kelvin scale**
conduction   radiation   contraction   **Celsius scale**   calorie

Use vocabulary words to complete the puzzle.

Heat

ACROSS

2 the transfer of heat that happens when molecules move

3 the scale on which 0 means the kinetic energy is zero

6 the scale with 32° as the freezing point and 212° as the boiling point of water

8 the heat transfer by energy waves

9 an increase in volume

DOWN

1 a decrease in volume

2 the heat transfer that occurs when molecules have direct contact

4 the energy needed to raise 1 gram of water 1° Celsius

5 the scale with 0° as the freezing point and 100° as the boiling point of water

7 the moving of heat from a cooler substance to a warmer one

 Tell someone in your family what you have learned about heat.

    93

Heat

LESSON 11

Sound Energy

(Student Book pages 64–69)

Lesson Summary Vibrations create sound waves that are made up of a pattern of particles pushed together and spread apart. Sound, which cannot travel through a vacuum, travels at different speeds through various mediums. The volume of sound is measured in decibels. The pitch of sound depends on the frequency, the number of waves passing a point in a given time. Frequency is measured in hertz. Sound above the range of human hearing is ultrasound. Sonar uses ultrasound and echoes for underwater exploration.

TARGET VOCABULARY

vibration an up-and-down or back-and-forth movement

vacuum a place empty of matter

medium the matter that sound travels through

volume loudness

decibel a unit of measure to describe volume

pitch how high or low sound is

hertz a unit of measure for pitch

ultrasound sound above the range of human hearing

echo the reflection of sound waves

sonar the use of ultrasound and echoes for underwater exploration

COGNATES

Spanish-speaking students may find a discussion of the similarities and differences between English and Spanish cognates helpful.

English	Spanish
vibration	vibración
vacuum	vacío
medium	medio
volume	volumen
hertz	hercio
ultrasound	ultrasonido
echo	eco
sonar	sónar

BEFORE READING

Activate Prior Knowledge

Bring in or have students bring in some simple musical instruments, such as a drum, a triangle, a tambourine, sticks, a clarinet, and so on. Have students experiment with these items to observe that the vibrations each instrument makes begin with the player's action, such as tapping or blowing. Encourage students to try to observe the actual movement of each instrument, if possible. Explain that vibrations, the up-and-down or back-and-forth movements, create the sound waves that they hear.

Introduce Target Vocabulary

Tell students they are about to read a selection about sound energy. Write the target vocabulary words on the board. Model the pronunciation of each word and have student volunteers repeat the word. Discuss the meaning of each word and, if necessary, write the definition next to the word.

Present Graphic Organizer

Provide each student with a copy of Vocabulary Graphic Organizer: Four Square, Teacher Guide page 78. Have students choose or assign each student a target vocabulary word. As they read, students should add information about the vocabulary word to the graphic organizer.

Word and Definition Cards
for Lesson 11 are on pages 119 and 120
of the Teacher Guide.

VOCABULARY STRATEGY: Using Illustrations

Tell students that pictures, photographs, diagrams, charts, and other illustrations, especially in textbooks, can provide readers with information to help them understand unknown words and concepts. Look over illustrations in the lesson with students. Point out that the sound wave diagram, page 64, helps them visualize a sound wave vibration; the chart of speed of sound, page 64, lists some mediums sound travels through; the table of volumes, page 65, shows common sounds and their decibel value; and the diagram on sonar, page 65, demonstrates how sonar works.

Sound Energy

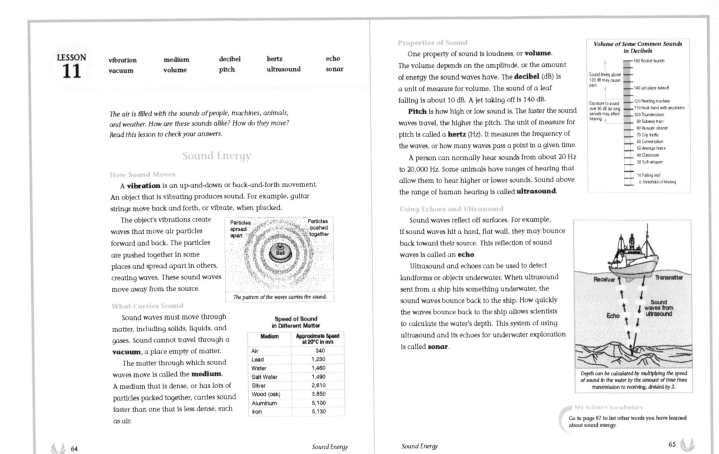

LESSON 11

| vibration | medium | decibel | hertz | echo |
| vacuum | volume | pitch | ultrasound | sonar |

The air is filled with the sounds of people, machines, animals, and weather. How are these sounds alike? How do they move? Read this lesson to check your answers.

Sound Energy

How Sound Moves

A **vibration** is an up-and-down or back-and-forth movement. An object that is vibrating produces sound. For example, guitar strings move back and forth, or vibrate, when plucked.

The object's vibrations create waves that move air particles forward and back. The particles are pushed together in some places and spread apart in others, creating waves. These sound waves move away from the source.

The pattern of the waves carries the sound.

What Carries Sound

Sound waves must move through matter, including solids, liquids, and gases. Sound cannot travel through a **vacuum**, a place empty of matter.

The matter through which sound waves move is called the **medium**. A medium that is dense, or has lots of particles packed together, carries sound faster than one that is less dense, such as air.

Speed of Sound in Different Matter

Medium	Approximate Speed at 20°C in m/s
Air	340
Lead	1,230
Water	1,460
Salt Water	1,490
Silver	2,610
Wood (oak)	3,850
Aluminum	5,100
Iron	5,130

64   *Sound Energy*

Properties of Sound

One property of sound is loudness, or **volume**. The volume depends on the amplitude, or the amount of energy the sound waves have. The **decibel** (dB) is a unit of measure for volume. The sound of a leaf falling is about 10 dB. A jet taking off is 140 dB.

Pitch is how high or low sound is. The faster the sound waves travel, the higher the pitch. The unit of measure for pitch is called a **hertz** (Hz). It measures the frequency of the waves, or how many waves pass a point in a given time.

A person can normally hear sounds from about 20 Hz to 20,000 Hz. Some animals have ranges of hearing that allow them to hear higher or lower sounds. Sound above the range of human hearing is called **ultrasound**.

Using Echoes and Ultrasound

Sound waves reflect off surfaces. For example, if sound waves hit a hard, flat wall, they may bounce back toward their source. This reflection of sound waves is called an **echo**.

Ultrasound and echoes can be used to detect landforms or objects underwater. When ultrasound sent from a ship hits something underwater, the sound waves bounce back to the ship. How quickly the waves bounce back to the ship allows scientists to calculate the water's depth. This system of using ultrasound and its echoes for underwater exploration is called **sonar**.

Volume of Some Common Sounds in Decibels

- 180 Rocket launch
- 140 Jet plane takeoff
- 120 Riveting machine
- 110 Rock band with amplifiers
- 100 Thunderstorm
- 90 Subway train
- 80 Vacuum cleaner
- 70 City traffic
- 60 Conversation
- 50 Average home
- 40 Classroom
- 30 Soft whisper
- 10 Falling leaf
- 0 Threshold of hearing

Sound levels above 120 dB may cause pain.

Exposure to sound over 90 dB for long periods may affect hearing.

Depth can be calculated by multiplying the speed of sound in the water by the amount of time from transmission to receiving, divided by 2.

My Science Vocabulary

Go to page 97 to list other words you have learned about sound energy.

Sound Energy   65

DURING READING

Read the selection aloud to students, stopping at the end of each paragraph or section. Review any words or concepts that students are having trouble with. Remind students that there is a glossary at the back of their book that contains all of the words that appear in boldfaced type in the lesson.

- Have students find in the dictionary other meanings for *medium (in the middle, a person telling fortunes, a means of communication, the surrounding environment, etc.)*; and for *pitch (the throw of a ball, a downward slant, sticky residue of coal tar, highest point on a building)*.

- Tell students that *decibel* is made up of the prefix *deci-*, which means "one-tenth," and *bel*, for Alexander Graham Bell, 1847–1922, the American inventor who patented the first telephone. The abbreviation for *decibel* is *dB*. The *hertz* (Hz) is based on the name of the scientist Heinrich Rudolf Hertz, 1857–1894, who defined the hertz. Have students note the capitalization that is retained on the initial of the proper name in each abbreviation.

- Ask if students know the derivation of *sonar*. Tell them that it is similar to the derivation of words such as *radar*, *NASA*, and *laser*. Explain that *sonar* is an acronym, a word made up of the initial letter or letters of a name or a series of words. *Sonar* takes its letters from *[so]und [na]vigation [r]anging*.

Have students read the selection again on their own.

AFTER READING

Review Graphic Organizers

Answer any questions students have about the reading selection. Then have students complete or review their graphic organizer and share it with the class.

Summarize

Have students work together to come up with either a written or an oral summary of the lesson. Encourage students to use the target vocabulary words as the basis of their summary. Have students share their summary with the class.

My Science Vocabulary

Encourage students to turn to My Science Vocabulary on page 97 of the student book and use the space provided to add other words about sound energy.

Sound Energy

A. Match each word with its meaning. Write the letter of the correct meaning on the line in front of each word.

1. _e_ decibel
2. _g_ sonar
3. _d_ vibration
4. _j_ volume
5. _i_ pitch
6. _b_ hertz
7. _f_ vacuum
8. _c_ ultrasound
9. _h_ echo
10. _a_ medium

a. the matter through which sound waves move
b. a unit used to measure pitch
c. sound above the range of human hearing
d. an up-and-down or back-and-forth movement
e. a unit used to measure the volume of sound
f. a place empty of matter
g. a system that uses ultrasound and its echoes for underwater exploration
h. the reflection of sound waves
i. how high or low sound is, based on the frequency of the sound waves
j. how loud sound is, based on the amplitude of the sound waves

B. Circle the word that makes sense in each sentence. Then write the word.

1. The volume of sound can be measured using the (vibration, **decibel**). _____decibel_____
2. When a ship sends out (**ultrasound**, hertz), the sound waves bounce back if they hit something underwater. _____ultrasound_____
3. If sound waves hit a hard, flat wall and reflect back, you may hear their (medium, **echo**). _____echo_____
4. The movement of a guitar string back and forth is a (sonar, **vibration**). _____vibration_____
5. Sound waves travel faster through a dense (pitch, **medium**) like wood. _____medium_____
6. The faster the sound waves travel, the higher the (vacuum, **pitch**) of the sound. _____pitch_____
7. Sound cannot travel through a (medium, **vacuum**). _____vacuum_____
8. Using ultrasound and its reflected sound waves to measure ocean depth is called (**sonar**, volume). _____sonar_____
9. The unit used to measure the frequency of waves is the (**hertz**, decibel). _____hertz_____
10. The loudness of sound is its (pitch, **volume**). _____volume_____

WORD ROOT

The word **vacuum** is based on the Latin word **vacuus**, which means "empty."

ACTIVITIES A–D

Encourage students to complete as many of the activities as possible. Remind students that they may refer to the Glossary at the back of their book as they complete the activities. Students may work independently, in small groups, or as a class. When students are done, discuss the answers for each activity.

Extensions

These extension ideas allow you to reuse or expand upon the activities. Share them with students who complete the activities before other students, or have students do them for additional practice with the target vocabulary words.

A   Turn each matching set into a complete sentence.

B   Circle each prepositional phrase in the sentences and draw an arrow to the word the phrase describes. Look for these prepositions: *above, of, off, through.*

WORD ROOT

Explain that a vacuum is an area of space that is empty of matter, or has very little matter. Ask if students know of another meaning of *vacuum (a vacuum cleaner)*. Have volunteers explain how that meaning relates to "empty." (*A vacuum cleaner pulls dirt by suction into an empty, or partially empty, bag.*)

C   Find five sentences that have action verbs, such as *travel*, not linking verbs, such as *is*. Use a different action verb to rewrite each of these five action-verb sentences without changing the meaning of the sentence.

D   Choose one sentence you wrote and draw a picture or diagram to illustrate the sentence.

| vibration | medium | decibel | hertz | echo |
| vacuum | volume | pitch | ultrasound | sonar |

C. *Write the vocabulary word that best completes each pair of sentences.*

1. A place empty of matter is a _____ vacuum _____ .
   Sound cannot travel through a _____ vacuum _____ .

2. The unit that measures the volume of sound is the _____ decibel _____ .
   The volume of a soft sound could be one _____ decibel _____ .

3. The system of using the reflection of ultrasound for underwater
   exploration is called _____ sonar _____ .
   Information from _____ sonar _____ can help scientists
   calculate water depth.

4. The unit of measure for pitch is the _____ hertz _____ .
   Humans can hear sounds at about 20 _____ hertz _____ .

5. A sound above the human range of hearing is called
   _____ ultrasound _____ .
   Sonar makes use of echoes and _____ ultrasound _____ .

6. The matter sound moves through is its _____ medium _____ .
   The _____ medium _____ for sound waves can be a solid, liquid, or gas.

7. Faster sound waves create a higher _____ pitch _____ .
   The _____ pitch _____ is how high or low a sound is.

8. A back-and-forth movement is a _____ vibration _____ .
   Plucking a guitar string causes a _____ vibration _____ .

9. The loudness of sound is its _____ volume _____ .
   The amplitude of the sound waves determines the _____ volume _____ .

10. The reflection of sound waves is an _____ echo _____ .
    Sound waves hitting a hard, flat wall may cause an _____ echo _____ .

68   Sound Energy

| vibration | medium | decibel | hertz | echo |
| vacuum | volume | pitch | ultrasound | sonar |

Students' answers will vary.

D. *Use each pair of words in a sentence.*

1. echo, sonar
   Ships use sonar to locate underwater objects by sending out ultrasound
   and picking up each echo that bounces back from something the sound
   waves hit.

2. vacuum, medium
   The medium through which sound travels cannot be a vacuum.

3. vibration, volume
   The vibration of an object creates sound waves, and their amplitude,
   or energy, determines the volume.

4. hertz, decibel
   A decibel measures the volume of sound, and a hertz measures
   the pitch.

5. pitch, ultrasound
   Sound with a pitch higher than humans can hear is called ultrasound.

Write!
Write your response to the prompt on a separate sheet of paper.
Use as many vocabulary words as you can in your writing.

Imagine first you are somewhere on land, and then in a ship on the water.
What sounds do you hear or use in each place? How can they be measured?

Sound Energy   69

Write!

Distribute Writing Graphic Organizer: Narrative Map,
Teacher Guide page 82. Have students work with a
partner or in a small group to brainstorm ideas for
writing. Tell students that they are writing a first-
person story, so they will be the main character.
Setting(s) should include one place on land and one
on the water. Main events should include what occurs.

Sample Answer

*First, I listen to some birds in the forest. The pitch
of this red bird is high but not higher than 20,000 hertz
because I can hear it. The volume of this large blue bird
is probably more than 30 decibels. The bird's sound
vibrations are traveling though the medium of air,
which is not a vacuum.*

*Now I am in a ship that uses ultrasound and its echo to
locate a sunken treasure on the ocean floor. The sonar tells
us to look on the level ocean floor deep below our ship.*

TAKE-HOME ACTIVITY

Assign the Take-Home Activity to students for
additional practice with the target vocabulary words.
The reproducible Take-Home Activity for Lesson 11
is on page 94 of the Teacher Guide.

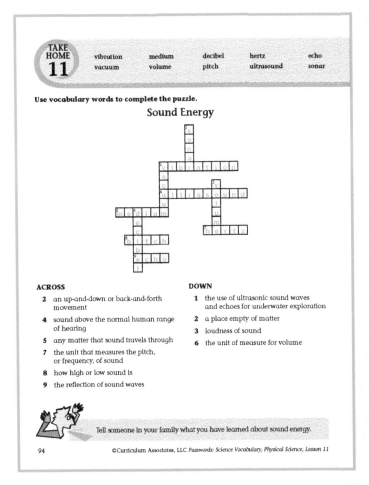

TAKE HOME 11

| vibration | medium | decibel | hertz | echo |
| vacuum | volume | pitch | ultrasound | sonar |

Use vocabulary words to complete the puzzle.

Sound Energy

ACROSS

2 an up-and-down or back-and-forth movement

4 sound above the normal human range of hearing

5 any matter that sound travels through

7 the unit that measures the pitch, or frequency, of sound

8 how high or low sound is

9 the reflection of sound waves

DOWN

1 the use of ultrasonic sound waves and echoes for underwater exploration

2 a place empty of matter

3 loudness of sound

6 the unit of measure for volume

Tell someone in your family what you have learned about sound energy.

94   ©Curriculum Associates, LLC Passwords: Science Vocabulary, Physical Science, Lesson 11

Sound Energy   59

LESSON 12
Light Energy

(Student Book pages 70–75)

TARGET VOCABULARY

electromagnetic spectrum the total range of radiant energy, such as light, x-rays, and radio waves

visible light the electromagnetic waves people see

prism a triangle-shaped piece of glass that bends light

infrared radiation electromagnetic waves with a longer wavelength than visible light

ultraviolet light electromagnetic waves with a shorter wavelength than visible light

opaque blocking light

translucent letting some light through

transparent letting almost all light through

convex lens a lens thicker at the center than the edges

concave lens a lens thinner at the center than the edges

COGNATES

Spanish-speaking students may find a discussion of the similarities and differences between English and Spanish cognates helpful.

English	Spanish
electromagnetic spectrum	espectro electromagnético
prism	prisma
infrared radiation	radiación infrarroja
ultraviolet light	luz ultravioleta
opaque	opaco
translucent	translúcido
transparent	transparente
convex lens	lente convexo
concave lens	lente cóncavo

Lesson Summary Visible light is a form of radiant energy on the electromagnetic spectrum. When white light enters a prism, the colors, each with its own wavelength, bend into a rainbow. Infrared radiation has a longer wavelength and slower frequency than visible light, while ultraviolet light has a shorter wavelength and faster frequency. Based upon how they transmit light, objects are opaque, translucent, or transparent. A convex lens bends light towards the center. A concave lens bends light away from the center.

BEFORE READING

Activate Prior Knowledge

Bring in or have students bring in a prism, a clear crystal, a rainbow maker, or any other object that refracts light into a rainbow. Show students the light source (such as the sun or an electric light) and the rainbow. Have students list the colors (*red, orange, yellow, green, blue, indigo, and violet*). Ask students to name something in nature that acts like a prism to create a rainbow. (*Raindrops and the sun form a rainbow in the sky.*)

Introduce Target Vocabulary

Tell students they are about to read a selection about light energy. Write the target vocabulary words on the board. Model the pronunciation of each word and have student volunteers repeat the word. Discuss the meaning of each word and, if necessary, write the definition next to the word.

Present Graphic Organizer

Provide each student with a copy of Vocabulary Graphic Organizer: Four Square, Teacher Guide page 78. Assign a target vocabulary word to each student. Have them write their word in the center. As students read, students should add information about their word to the graphic organizer.

Word and Definition Cards
for Lesson 12 are on pages 121 and 122
of the Teacher Guide.

VOCABULARY STRATEGY: Prefixes

Write the words *translucent* and *transparent* on the board. Refer students to the definitions of these words in the Glossary. Ask them what the meanings of the words have in common. (*They have to do with what happens to light passing through an object.*) Explain that the prefix *trans-* means "through." *Translucent* combines the prefix *trans-* with *lucere*, which means "to shine." *Transparent* combines *trans-* with *parere*, which means "to show." Have students restate the definition of each word (*translucent, letting some light shine through; transparent, letting most of the light shine through so objects show*). Encourage students to add these words to the root words chart on page 99 and the prefix chart on page 100 of their book.

Light Energy

LESSON 12

electromagnetic spectrum   infrared radiation   translucent   convex lens
visible light   ultraviolet light   transparent   concave lens
prism   opaque

Do you know how light travels? Do you know why light can make a rainbow? Read this lesson to learn more about light energy.

Light Energy

Electromagnetic Waves

Light is radiant energy. It travels in waves that produce electric and magnetic fields. The total range of radiant energy, or electromagnetic waves, is called the **electromagnetic spectrum**.

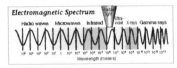

Visible Light

Visible light is all the electromagnetic waves that people can see. Visible light appears white to the eye but is actually made of many colors. Each color has a different frequency and wavelength. Frequency is how many waves move past a point in a given time. Wavelength is the distance between the crest, or top, of one wave and the next.

You can see the colors in white light by using a prism. A **prism** is a triangle-shaped piece of glass that bends light. The prism bends each color of light a slightly different amount. Red light, which has a long wavelength, is bent the least. Violet light is bent the most.

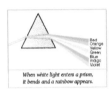

When white light enters a prism, it bends and a rainbow appears.

Infrared Radiation and Ultraviolet Light

Infrared radiation and ultraviolet light are part of the invisible spectrum. **Infrared radiation** has a longer wavelength and slower frequency than visible light. When the sun heats your skin, you are feeling infrared radiation. **Ultraviolet light** has a shorter wavelength and faster frequency than visible light. Most ultraviolet light comes from the sun.

Transmitting Light

All objects reflect, or bounce back, some light, or you would not see them. An object that is **opaque** blocks light. Most of the light that hits the object is absorbed. It does not allow light to pass through. You cannot see through an opaque object.

A **translucent** object lets some light through and scatters some light. You can see light through a translucent object, but not sharp images.

A **transparent** object lets almost all the light that strikes the surface pass through. You can see a clear image through a transparent object.

The black frame of this window is opaque, the middle panel is transparent, and the side panels are translucent.

Lenses

A lens is a transparent object with a surface that bends light rays as they pass through. A **convex lens** is thicker at the center than at the edges. Light rays that enter a convex lens bend toward the center.

A **concave lens** is thinner at the center than at the edges. Light rays passing through bend away from the center, toward the thicker part of the lens.

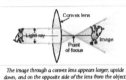

The image through a convex lens appears larger, upside down, and on the opposite side of the lens from the object.

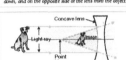

The image through a concave lens appears smaller, right-side up, and on the same side of the lens as the object.

My Science Vocabulary

Go to page 97 to list other words you have learned about light energy.

DURING READING

Read the selection aloud to students, stopping at the end of each paragraph or section. Review any words or concepts that students are having trouble with. Remind students that there is a glossary at the back of their book that contains all of the words that appear in boldfaced type in the lesson.

- Refer students to the diagram of the electromagnetic spectrum on page 70. Starting at the left, have them point to the section of the spectrum that represents each of the following: *radio waves, microwaves, infrared radiation, visible light, ultraviolet light, x-rays,* and *gamma rays.* Tell students that *infrared* comes from *infra-*, which means "below" + *red. Ultraviolet* comes from *ultra-*, which means "beyond" + *violet.* Help students see that these names reflect the placement of infrared radiation and ultraviolet light on either side of visible light on the electromagnetic spectrum.

- To help students differentiate convex and concave, tell them that *convex* comes from the Latin root *convexus,* which means "arched"; *concave* comes

from the root *cavus,* which means "hollow." Point out that although *lens* ends in *-s,* it is a singular noun. Ask students for the plural form *(lenses).*

Have students read the selection again on their own.

AFTER READING

Review Graphic Organizers

Answer any questions students have about the reading selection. Then have students complete or review their graphic organizer and share it with the class.

Summarize

Have students work together to come up with either a written or an oral summary of the lesson. Encourage students to use the target vocabulary words as the basis of their summary. Have students share their summary with the class.

My Science Vocabulary

Encourage students to turn to My Science Vocabulary on page 97 of the student book and use the space provided to add other words about light energy.

electromagnetic spectrum   infrared radiation   translucent   convex lens
visible light   ultraviolet light   transparent   concave lens
prism   opaque

A. *Fill in the blanks with the correct vocabulary word.*

1. a triangle-shaped piece of glass that bends white light into its colors
   p r i s m

2. radiant energy with a longer wavelength and slower frequency than visible light
   i n f r a r e d   r a d i a t i o n

3. letting some light through and scattering some light
   t r a n s l u c e n t

4. a lens thicker at the center than at the edges
   c o n v e x   l e n s

5. the total range of radiant energy, which travels in electromagnetic waves
   e l e c t r o m a g n e t i c
   s p e c t r u m

6. a lens thinner at the center than at the edges
   c o n c a v e   l e n s

7. all the electromagnetic waves that people can see
   v i s i b l e   l i g h t

8. radiant energy with a shorter wavelength and faster frequency than visible light
   u l t r a v i o l e t   l i g h t

9. letting almost all light pass through
   t r a n s p a r e n t

10. not allowing light to pass through
    o p a q u e

72   *Light Energy*

Light Energy

electromagnetic spectrum   infrared radiation   translucent   convex lens
visible light   ultraviolet light   transparent   concave lens
prism   opaque

B. *Circle the word that makes sense in each sentence. Then write the word.*

1. As part of the invisible spectrum, (infrared radiation, ultraviolet radiation) has a longer wavelength than visible light. _____ infrared radiation _____

2. An object that blocks light is (opaque, translucent). _____ opaque _____

3. A lens that bends light rays toward the center is a (concave lens, convex lens). _____ convex lens _____

4. Radio waves are a form of radiant energy in the (ultraviolet light, electromagnetic spectrum). _____ electromagnetic spectrum _____

5. The only group of electromagnetic waves that people can see is (infrared light, visible light). _____ visible light _____

6. When white light passes through a (prism, convex lens), a rainbow appears. _____ prism _____

7. A lens is a (translucent, transparent) object. _____ transparent _____

8. A form of radiant energy with a shorter wavelength than visible light is (ultraviolet light, electromagnetic spectrum). _____ ultraviolet light _____

9. A lens that bends light rays away from the center is a (convex lens, concave lens). _____ concave lens _____

10. You can see light through a (transparent, translucent) object, but not sharp images. _____ translucent _____

ROOT
The word **opaque** comes from the Latin word **opacus**, meaning "dark."

73   *Light Energy*

ACTIVITIES A–D

Encourage students to complete as many of the activities as possible. Remind students that they may refer to the Glossary at the back of their book as they complete the activities. Students may work independently, in small groups, or as a class. When students are done, discuss the answers for each activity.

Extensions

These extension ideas allow you to reuse or expand upon the activities. Share them with students who complete the activities before other students, or have students do them for additional practice with the target vocabulary words.

A For each target vocabulary word, draw a picture or diagram that could replace the written definition.

B Circle the nouns in each sentence.

C Write *N* above each target vocabulary word that is a noun, and write *ADJ* above each one that is an adjective.

D Group the target vocabulary words into three or more categories. Write a title for each group.

WORD ROOT

Ask students to explain how "dark" relates to the word *opaque* (an opaque object does not let light through, so it is dark). Point out that *opaque* is also used to mean "dense" or "hard to understand." Unlike an "opaque object" that is literally dark, in these other usages, *dark* is meant figuratively.

electromagnetic spectrum infrared radiation translucent convex lens
visible light   ultraviolet light   transparent
prism   opaque   concave lens

C. *Choose the correct vocabulary word to complete each sentence.*

1. Wood lets no light pass through it, so it is ____opaque____ .

2. Images appear larger through a ____convex lens____ because it bends light toward the center.

3. Many forms of radiant energy, such as radio waves, x-rays, and microwaves, make up the ____electromagnetic spectrum____ .

4. A glass window will let most light through if it is completely ____transparent____ .

5. Electromagnetic waves with a longer wavelength and a slower frequency than light is ____infrared radiation____ .

6. Light is bent toward the edges of a ____concave lens____ , making images appear smaller.

7. When white light passes through a ____prism____ , red light bends the least and violet light bends the most.

8. White light is made of all the colors of ____visible light____ .

9. The form of radiant energy on the invisible spectrum with a shorter wavelength than visible light is ____ultraviolet light____ .

10. If a plastic cover is ____translucent____ , you can see some light through it, but not a sharp image.

74 Light Energy

Light Energy 75

electromagnetic spectrum infrared radiation translucent convex lens
visible light   ultraviolet light   transparent
prism   opaque   concave lens

D. *Use each word in a sentence that shows you understand the meaning of the word.*

1. concave lens _A concave lens is thinner at the center than at the edges, so light is bent toward the edges._

2. translucent _Frosted glass is translucent because it only lets some light through._

3. visible light _All the colors of visible light are just a very small part of the electromagnetic spectrum._

4. prism _A prism bends white light to make a rainbow._

5. convex lens _A convex lens bends light rays toward its center, which is thicker than at the edges._

6. electromagnetic spectrum _The full range of radiant energy, which includes visible light, is called the electromagnetic spectrum._

7. ultraviolet light _Ultraviolet light has a shorter wavelength than visible light and comes from the sun._

8. opaque _The walls of most homes are opaque._

9. transparent _A lens must be transparent so that light moves through it easily._

10. infrared radiation _The radiant energy that you feel when the sun heats your skin is infrared radiation._

 Write!

Write your response to the prompt on a separate sheet of paper. Use as many vocabulary words as you can in your writing.

Imagine that you can experiment with being different forms of radiant energy. What might you be and what might you do?

Write!

Distribute Writing Graphic Organizer: Narrative Map, Teacher Guide page 82. Have students work with a partner or in a small group to brainstorm ideas for writing. Students can create a character, or they can be the main character. Setting(s) should include what is around them as they experiment. Main events should include what occurs.

Sample Answer

I start as visible light. I see an object, and I'm absorbed. The object is opaque. I try again and find a translucent door. I scatter as I go through. Then I try something transparent. In a convex lens, I'm bent toward the center. In a concave lens, I'm bent toward the edges.

Now, I want to try being some other radiant energy on the electromagnetic spectrum. I take on a shorter wavelength than visible light and become ultraviolet light. Next, I make my wavelength longer, and become infrared light.

TAKE-HOME ACTIVITY

Assign the Take-Home Activity to students for additional practice with the target vocabulary words. The reproducible Take-Home Activity for Lesson 12 is on page 95 of the Teacher Guide.

Light Energy 63

TAKE HOME 12

electromagnetic spectrum infrared radiation translucent convex lens
visible light   ultraviolet light   transparent concave lens
prism   opaque

Use vocabulary words to complete the puzzle.

Light Energy

ACROSS

2 the total range of radiant energy
4 letting almost all light pass through
5 letting some light pass through
6 a lens that is thinner at the center than at the edges
7 the part of the electromagnetic spectrum that people can see
9 radiant energy with a longer wavelength than visible light

DOWN

1 radiant energy with a shorter wavelength than visible light
3 a lens that is thicker at the center than at the edges
8 a triangle-shaped piece of glass that bends light
10 blocking light

 Tell someone in your family what you have learned about light energy.

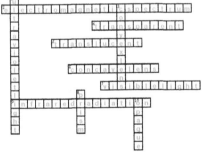

LESSON 13

Electricity

(Student Book pages 76–81)

TARGET VOCABULARY

conductor a material that lets electricity through

insulator a material that blocks electricity

resistance how much a substance opposes electricity

ohm a unit of measure of resistance

electric circuit a complete path for electricity

battery a device that uses chemical energy to make electricity

series circuit a circuit with only one path

parallel circuit a circuit with two or more paths

direct current current that flows in one direction

alternating current current that switches direction rapidly

COGNATES

Spanish-speaking students may find a discussion of the similarities and differences between English and Spanish cognates helpful.

English	Spanish
conductor	conductor
insulator	aislador
resistance	resistencia
electric circuit	circuito eléctrico
battery	batería
series circuit	circuito serie
parallel circuit	circuito paralelo
alternating current	corriente alterna

VOCABULARY STRATEGY: Multimeaning Words

Several of the target vocabulary words have more than one meaning. Remind students that context clues can help them determine which meaning of the word should be applied. These clues can be words the writer chose to define or explain the unknown word. Clues are also provided by the situation in which the word appears. For example, since the lesson is a science lesson about electricity, *conductor* means a material that allows electricity to pass through, not a person driving a train. Have students find and explain other target vocabulary words whose meaning is made clear by the situation. (*Battery is a device to make electricity, not a series of tests or a beating; resistance is opposing electricity not a political group fighting for independence, etc.*)

Lesson Summary Electricity, the flow of electric charges, moves through conductors but not insulators. Resistance, measured in ohms, is how much a substance opposes the flow of electricity. Electricity flows in an electric circuit. A battery can provide current for a circuit. Circuits can be wired with appliances in series, with only one path to follow, or in parallel, with two or more paths. Current from a battery is direct current. Household current switches direction rapidly and is called alternating current.

BEFORE READING

Activate Prior Knowledge

Ask students to name everything they can think of that uses electricity and write the list on the board. Then have students read the paragraph above the title of the lesson. Ask volunteers to explain what they think electricity is. Write their ideas on the board and revise them as students read the lesson.

Introduce Target Vocabulary

Tell students they are about to read a selection about electricity. Write the target vocabulary words on the board. Model the pronunciation of each word and have student volunteers repeat the word. Discuss the meaning of each word and, if necessary, write the definition next to the word.

Present Graphic Organizer

Provide each student with a copy of Vocabulary Graphic Organizer: Word Web, Teacher Guide page 76. Have students write *Electricity* in the center circle of the web. As they read the lesson, have students group related target vocabulary words in the outer circles. Have them write a phrase next to each circle that explains why they grouped the words together.

Word and Definition Cards
for Lesson 13 are on pages 123 and 124
of the Teacher Guide.

Electricity

conductor   resistance   electric circuit   series circuit   direct current
insulator   ohm   battery   parallel circuit alternating current

You know that wires carry electricity, batteries make electricity, and lightning is a form of electricity. Do you know what electricity is? Read this lesson to find out.

Electricity

Flow of Electrons

Electricity is energy from charged particles. The flow of electric charges occurs because of excess electrons. An electron is the tiniest of the three main particles in an atom. Electrons have a negative charge and flow toward an area with a positive charge. This flow of electrons is called an electric current.

Conductors and Insulators

An electric current can flow along a wire made of a conductor. A **conductor** is a material, such as metal, that lets electrons pass through it easily. The outside of a wire is often covered with an insulator. An **insulator** does not let electricity pass through it easily. It keeps the electric charges from flowing out of the wire.

Resistance is how much a substance opposes the flow of electrons. The unit of measure for resistance is the **ohm**. A good conductor has little resistance. A good insulator has a lot.

Lightning is a form of electricity. It occurs when negative electric charges build up at the base of thunderclouds and then jump to the ground.

Conductors	Insulators
Silver	Rubber
Copper	Glass
Gold	Plastic
Aluminum	Wood
Iron	Brick
Lead	Fabric

Circuits

Electric current can only flow in a complete path, such as from a place with a negative charge to a place with a positive charge. This complete path is called an **electric circuit**.

For example, a battery and wires can make an electric circuit. A **battery** uses chemical energy to make electricity. The chemicals inside a battery react to create an excess of electrons at the negative terminal. The electrons then flow through the wire from the negative terminal to the positive terminal.

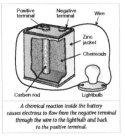

A chemical reaction inside the battery causes electrons to flow from the negative terminal through the wire to the lightbulb and back to the positive terminal.

Series and Parallel Circuits

Electric circuits can be wired in two ways. A **series circuit** has only one path for electricity to follow. Suppose three lightbulbs are wired to a battery in a series circuit. The electric current will flow through a single path of wires to each bulb. If one bulb burns out, the circuit is broken and none of the lights will work.

In a **parallel circuit**, electricity can follow two or more paths. So if three bulbs are connected in a parallel circuit, each bulb will have its own complete path to and from the battery. If one bulb burns out, the rest of the bulbs stay lit.

Series Circuit

Parallel Circuit

Direct and Alternating Current

The current from a battery is called **direct current** because it flows in only one direction, from the negative terminal to the positive terminal. Household electricity is **alternating current**. The current's flow switches direction rapidly, about 60 times a second.

My Science Vocabulary

Go to page 98 to list other words you have learned about electricity.

DURING READING

Read the selection aloud to students, stopping at the end of each paragraph or section. Review any words or concepts that students are having trouble with. Remind students that there is a glossary at the back of their book that contains all of the words that appear in boldfaced type in the lesson.

- From geography, students may know the word *peninsula*, "a point of land surrounded by water." Ask students which target vocabulary word uses the same root, *insula*, which means "island" (*insulator*). Ask how an insulator is like an island. *(It is set apart, or isolated, from electricity because it will not let it pass through.)*

- Students may be interested to learn that the ohm was named after Georg Simon Ohm, 1787–1854, a German physicist. *Ohm* is used to form the term *ohmage*, "the resistance in ohms," and *ohmmeter*, "the tool to measure ohms."

- Direct attention to the diagrams of the circuits on page 77. Starting with the series circuit, have students trace a path that electricity can follow. Ask how many paths they found and how many lights must be working *(one path, all three lights).*

Then have them trace paths electricity can follow in the parallel circuit. Ask how many paths they found and how many lights must be working *(more than one path, at least one light).*

Have students read the selection again on their own.

AFTER READING

Review Graphic Organizers

Answer any questions students have about the reading selection. Then have students complete or review their graphic organizer and share it with the class.

Summarize

Have students work together to come up with either a written or an oral summary of the lesson. Encourage students to use the target vocabulary words as the basis of their summary. Have students share their summary with the class.

My Science Vocabulary

Encourage students to turn to My Science Vocabulary on page 98 of the student book and use the space provided to add other words about electricity.

A. *Fill in the blanks with the correct vocabulary word.*

1. a material that lets electrons pass through it easily
   c o n d u c t o r

2. how much a substance opposes the flow of electrons
   r e s i s t a n c e

3. an electric current that flows in only one direction
   d i r e c t   c u r r e n t

4. a circuit in which electricity can follow two or more paths
   p a r a l l e l   c i r c u i t

5. a device that uses chemical energy to make electricity
   b a t t e r y

6. a circuit with only one path for electricity to follow
   s e r i e s   c i r c u i t

7. the unit of measure for resistance
   o h m

8. a material that does not let electricity pass through it easily
   i n s u l a t o r

9. a complete path along which an electric current flows
   e l e c t r i c   c i r c u i t

10. an electric current that switches direction rapidly
    a l t e r n a t i n g   c u r r e n t

B. *Choose and write the two words that best complete each sentence.*

| conductor | resistance | ohm | insulator |

1. Because electricity can flow through it easily, metal makes a good
   __conductor__ but a poor __insulator__ .

| series circuit | parallel circuit | alternating current | resistance |

2. Electricity follows only one path in a __series circuit__ ,
   but two or more paths in a __parallel circuit__ .

| insulator | ohm | battery | resistance |

3. The unit used to measure __resistance__ is the
   __ohm__ .

| electric circuit | alternating current | conductor | battery |

4. Using wires and a __battery__ , you can make
   an __electric circuit__ that carries direct current.

| ohm | alternating current | direct current | series circuit |

5. Current flowing in only one direction is __direct current__ ,
   but current that switches direction rapidly is __alternating current__ .

ROOT
The word **conductor** is based on the Latin word **conducere**, which means "to escort, or to lead together."

ACTIVITIES A–D

Encourage students to complete as many of the activities as possible. Remind students that they may refer to the Glossary at the back of their book as they complete the activities. Students may work independently, in small groups, or as a class. When students are done, discuss the answers for each activity.

Extensions

These extension ideas allow you to reuse or expand upon the activities. Share them with students who complete the activities before other students, or have students do them for additional practice with the target vocabulary words.

A Write all the target vocabulary words that have the prefixes *re-*, *con-* and the suffixes *-or*, *-ance*, *-ic*, *-ing*.

B Write the plural of each target vocabulary word. Watch out for one spelling change.

WORD ROOT

Ask students to explain how a conductor "escorts or leads together" electricity (*it allows electricity to move through it or along it, as in a wire*). Explain that *conducere* can be broken down further into the prefix *con-*, meaning "together," and the root *ducere*, "to lead."

C Mark each simple sentence (one subject and one verb) with an *S* for "simple." Mark each sentence that is not simple with *NS* for "not simple." Choose one sentence you marked *NS*, and rewrite it as two simple sentences.

D For each sentence, write a question that would be answered by your sentence.

conductor resistance electric circuit series circuit direct current
insulator ohm battery parallel circuit alternating current

C. *Choose the correct vocabulary word to complete each sentence.*

1. The current that comes from a battery and flows from the negative terminal to the positive terminal is _____direct current_____ .

2. A chemical reaction inside a _____battery_____ produces an electric current.

3. If one lightbulb in a _____series circuit_____ burns out, all the other bulbs will go out too.

4. The metal copper is a _____conductor_____ that is often used for electrical wires.

5. You can use the _____ohm_____ to measure the resistance of a rubber insulator to the flow of electrons.

6. A good conductor has little _____resistance_____ to the flow of electrons.

7. Household current is an _____alternating current_____ , which switches flow about 60 times a second.

8. If only one lightbulb goes out in a _____parallel circuit_____ , the rest of the bulbs stay lit because each has its own separate path.

9. An electrical wire is often covered in plastic, which is a good _____insulator_____ .

10. Electric current will flow only along a complete path known as an _____electric circuit_____ .

---

conductor resistance electric circuit series circuit direct current
insulator ohm battery parallel circuit alternating current

Students' answers will vary.

D. *Use each pair of words in a sentence.*

1. electric circuit, alternating current
   An alternating current flows through an electric circuit in a home.

2. conductor, insulator
   The metal in a wire is a conductor, while the plastic covering of the wire is an insulator.

3. battery, direct current
   A battery produces direct current, which flows in just one direction.

4. series circuit, parallel circuit
   A parallel circuit is better than a series circuit for lights in a home because the other lights will still shine even if one light burns out.

5. resistance, ohm
   An ohm is used to measure the resistance of a substance to the flow of electricity.

Write!

Write your response to the prompt on a separate sheet of paper. Use as many vocabulary words as you can in your writing.

Imagine you are an inventor working on the design for a new appliance. What decisions will you make to be sure that your product will work well?

Write!

Distribute Writing Graphic Organizer: Main Idea and Details Chart, Teacher Guide page 80. Have students work with a partner or in a small group to brainstorm ideas for writing. Tell students to write a main idea about what they are working on in the first Main Idea box and decisions they will make in the second Main Idea box. Have them write details to support their main ideas in the corresponding Details boxes.

Sample Answer

I will make two different products. One will operate from a battery and use direct current. The other will be designed for alternating current that is found in homes.

I'll need to make sure, first of all, that my wire is a good conductor, with a good insulator to protect it. I will check the resistance of the wire, and measure it in ohms. To wire my electric circuits, I will choose a parallel circuit rather than a series circuit, for more dependable operation.

TAKE-HOME ACTIVITY

Assign the Take-Home Activity to students for additional practice with the target vocabulary words. The reproducible Take-Home Activity for Lesson 13 is on page 96 of the Teacher Guide.

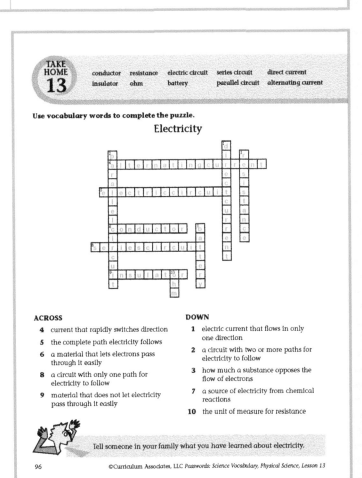

TAKE HOME 13

conductor resistance electric circuit series circuit direct current
insulator ohm battery parallel circuit alternating current

Use vocabulary words to complete the puzzle.

Electricity

ACROSS

4 current that rapidly switches direction
5 the complete path electricity follows
6 a material that lets electrons pass through it easily
8 a circuit with only one path for electricity to follow
9 material that does not let electricity pass through it easily

DOWN

1 electric current that flows in only one direction
2 a circuit with two or more paths for electricity to follow
3 how much a substance opposes the flow of electrons
7 a source of electricity from chemical reactions
10 the unit of measure for resistance

Tell someone in your family what you have learned about electricity.

96 ©Curriculum Associates, LLC *Passwords: Science Vocabulary, Physical Science, Lesson 13*

LESSON 14

Magnetism

(Student Book pages 82–87)

Lesson Summary Magnetism is a force produced by the motion of electric charges. All magnets have a north and south pole. Lines of force show that the magnetic field around the poles is more concentrated than in other parts. Like poles of magnets repel, and unlike poles attract. A permanent magnet keeps its magnetic properties. Using the interaction of electricity and magnetism, or electromagnetism, an electromagnet produces magnetism that can be turned on and off using an electric current.

TARGET VOCABULARY

magnetism a force produced by moving electric charges

magnetize to turn matter into a magnet

permanent magnet a magnet that remains magnetic

magnetic pole the strongest part of a magnet

attraction the pull toward each other

repulsion the push away from each other

magnetic field the region of force around a magnet

lines of force an illustration of the magnetic field

electromagnetism the interaction between electricity and magnetism

electromagnet a magnet that turns on and off

COGNATES

Spanish-speaking students may find a discussion of the similarities and differences between English and Spanish cognates helpful.

English	Spanish
magnetism	magnetismo
permanent magnet	imán permanente
magnetic pole	polo magnético
attraction	atracción
repulsion	repulsión
electromagnetism	electromagnetismo

VOCABULARY STRATEGY: Context Clues

Have students find all the target vocabulary words in this lesson that have definitions using *is* or *is called* (*magnetism, magnetic pole, attraction, magnetic field, electromagnetism*). Tell students that another context clue may be a synonym or a phrase with the same meaning. Have students find the two words defined in this way (*permanent magnet, repulsion*). Finally, have

BEFORE READING

Activate Prior Knowledge

Provide magnets for students to experiment with, or ask students to list some uses of magnets and write these on the board. Ask students to describe three things that might happen when a magnet is brought near another object. (*It might stick, it might be pushed away, or it might do nothing.*) Then have students read the paragraph above the title of the lesson. Encourage students to share what they know about how magnets work and how they can make electricity.

Introduce Target Vocabulary

Tell students they are about to read a selection about magnetism. Write the target vocabulary words on the board. Model the pronunciation of each word and have student volunteers repeat the word. Discuss the meaning of each word and, if necessary, write the definition next to the word.

Present Graphic Organizer

Provide each student with a copy of Vocabulary Graphic Organizer: Word Chart, Teacher Guide page 77. Assign each student a target vocabulary word. Have students fill in as much of the chart as they can. As they read the lesson, students should continue to add information to the chart.

Word and Definition Cards
for Lesson 14 are on pages 125 and 126
of the Teacher Guide.

students list the words for which the writer provides information but no exact definition or synonym and then define these words (*lines of force—a model of lines that show the magnetic field; electromagnet—a device that produces magnetism that can be turned on and off; wire coil—wire wrapped around the core of an electromagnet*).

Magnetism

LESSON 14

magnetism   **magnetic pole**   **magnetic field**   **electromagnetism**
permanent magnet   **attraction**   **lines of force**   **electromagnet**
magnetize   **repulsion**

You have probably played with magnets. Do you know how magnets work? Do you know that magnets can make electricity? Read this lesson to learn about magnetism.

Magnetism

Magnetism is a force produced by the motion of electrons within matter. Electrons are the tiny particles in atoms with negative electric charges.

In most matter, the electrons within the atoms move in all directions. In magnetic matter, the electrons line up.

A **permanent magnet** is one in which the charged particles stay lined up. It is possible to turn some types of matter into temporary magnets. For example, stroking a piece of iron with a permanent magnet many times will **magnetize** it.

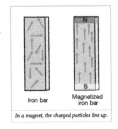

Iron bar   Magnetized iron bar

In a magnet, the charged particles line up.

Magnetic Poles

A **magnetic pole** is the place on a magnet where the magnetic force is strongest. Every magnet has two magnetic poles, a north pole and a south pole. For a bar magnet, the magnetic poles are at either end.

When two unlike poles are near, they pull toward each other. They exhibit **attraction**. Two like poles exhibit **repulsion**. They push away from each other.

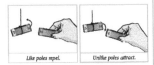

Like poles repel.   *Unlike poles attract.*

Magnetic Field

Even though it is strongest at the poles, the magnetic force extends over the whole magnet. This region of force around the magnet is the **magnetic field**.

Lines can be used to indicate the magnetic field around a magnet. These **lines of force** are closest together at the poles, where the field is strongest.

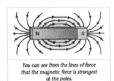

You can see from the lines of force that the magnetic force is strongest at the poles.

Electricity and Magnetism

The relationship between electricity and magnetism is called **electromagnetism**. Whenever electrons move, such as when an electric current flows through a wire, they create a magnetic field. In turn, whenever a magnet moves near a wire, it creates an electric current.

An **electromagnet** is a device that develops magnetism when an electric current passes through it. A simple electromagnet consists of a coil of wire wrapped around an iron nail. The ends of the wire are connected to the terminals of a battery. An electric current flows from the battery through the wire coil, producing a magnetic field around the nail. When the electric current is cut off, the nail loses its magnetism.

Negative (−) battery terminal   Battery   Positive (+) battery terminal

Wire coil   Iron nail

Larger electromagnets work in the same way as this simple electromagnet.

My Science Vocabulary

 Go to page 98 to list other words you have learned about magnetism.

82   Magnetism

Magnetism   83

DURING READING

Read the selection aloud to students, stopping at the end of each paragraph or section. Review any words or concepts that students are having trouble with. Remind students that there is a glossary at the back of their book that contains all of the words that appear in boldfaced type in the lesson.

- Have volunteers write on the board the target vocabulary words that include *magnet (magnetism, permanent magnet, magnetize, magnetic pole, magnetic field, electromagnetism,* and *electromagnet)*. Point out the suffix *-ism,* which means "a state or condition" and makes the nouns *magnetism* and *electromagnetism.* Point out the suffix *-ic,* which means "caused by" and makes the adjective *magnetic.* Encourage students to add these words to the suffix chart on page 100 of their book.

- Tell students that the suffix *-ion* means "action or result" and can make a verb into a noun. Ask students to list the target vocabulary words that use this suffix and each base verb *(attraction, attract; repulsion, repel).* Point out the spelling change from *e* to *u* in *repulsion.*

- Refer students to the diagram of lines of force on page 83. Have students find the two poles of the magnet and describe the pattern they see at each pole. *(The lines of force are more concentrated.)*

Have students read the selection again on their own.

AFTER READING

Review Graphic Organizers

Answer any questions students have about the reading selection. Then have students complete or review their graphic organizer and share it with the class.

Summarize

Have students work together to come up with either a written or an oral summary of the lesson. Encourage students to use the target vocabulary words as the basis of their summary. Have students share their summary with the class.

My Science Vocabulary

Encourage students to turn to My Science Vocabulary on page 98 of the student book and use the space provided to add other words about magnetism.

Magnetism   69

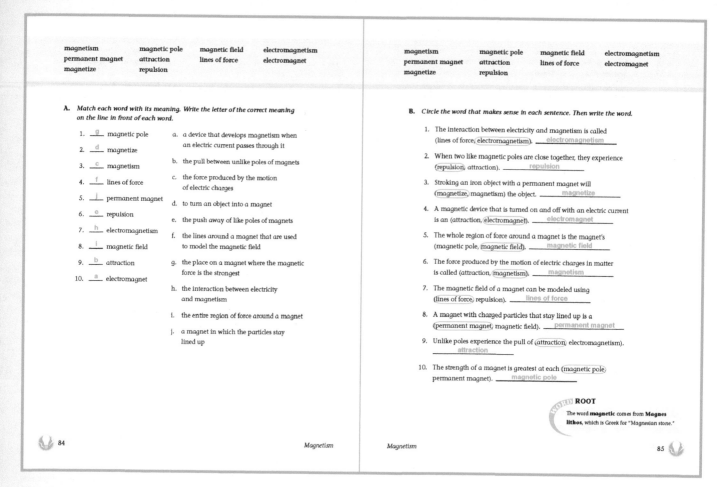

ACTIVITIES A–D

Encourage students to complete as many of the activities as possible. Remind students that they may refer to the Glossary at the back of their book as they complete the activities. Students may work independently, in small groups, or as a class. When students are done, discuss the answers for each activity.

Extensions

These extension ideas allow you to reuse or expand upon the activities. Share them with students who complete the activities before other students, or have students do them for additional practice with the target vocabulary words.

A Break each target vocabulary word into syllables. Draw a line between each syllable of each word.

B Renumber the sentences so that they are in alphabetical order by the target vocabulary words. Remember if the first word is the same, look at the second word.

WORD ROOT

Tell students that Magnesia was the name for a narrow, coastal section of Greece. The region, named for King Magnes, was a place that produced many metals, including lodestone, a magnetized piece of the mineral magnetite, or iron oxide.

C Circle all the prepositions and underline the prepositional phrases in each sentence. Draw a line to the word each phrase describes. Look for these prepositions: *around, by, in, of, on,* and *with.*

D Draw a simple diagram for which one of your sentences could be an appropriate caption.

magnetism   magnetic pole   magnetic field   electromagnetism
permanent magnet   attraction   lines of force   electromagnet
magnetize   repulsion

C. Choose the correct vocabulary word to complete each sentence.

1. If unlike poles of two magnets are brought close together, the ___attraction___ may pull the magnets together.

2. The region of magnetic force around a magnet is the ___magnetic field___.

3. The combined effects of electricity and magnetism are called ___electromagnetism___.

4. The magnetic field around an object is displayed using ___lines of force___.

5. The place on a magnet with the strongest force is a ___magnetic pole___.

6. Magnetic force, or ___magnetism___, is produced by the motion of electric charges.

7. Some magnets are temporary, but a ___permanent magnet___ is one in which the particles stay lined up.

8. It is possible to ___magnetize___ some types of matter, turning them into temporary magnets.

9. A device called an ___electromagnet___ produces magnetism that can be turned on and off with an electric current.

10. Either attraction or ___repulsion___ occurs when poles of magnets are brought close together.

86   *Magnetism*

---

magnetism   magnetic pole   magnetic field   electromagnetism
permanent magnet   attraction   lines of force   electromagnet
magnetize   repulsion

Students' answers will vary.

D. Use each pair of words in a sentence.

1. attraction, repulsion
Unlike poles of magnets experience attraction, but like poles experience repulsion.

2. magnetize, electromagnet
Running an electric current through an electromagnet will magnetize it.

3. magnetic field, lines of force
In the magnetic field, lines of force show where the field is strongest and weakest.

4. magnetic pole, permanent magnet
A permanent magnet has both a north magnetic pole and a south magnetic pole.

5. magnetism, electromagnetism
By studying electromagnetism, you can see the combined effects of magnetism and electricity.

 Write!
Write your response to the prompt on a separate sheet of paper. Use as many vocabulary words as you can in your writing.

You have been asked to teach a class about magnetism. What will you tell and show the class to help your students understand magnetism?

Magnetism   87

Write!

Distribute Writing Graphic Organizer: Idea Wheel, Teacher Guide page 81. Tell students to write *Magnetism* in the center of the wheel. Then on the spokes of the wheel, they should write things they will tell and show the class to help them understand magnetism.

Sample Answer

    I have here two permanent magnets, or bar magnets. You cannot see magnetism. But watch the attraction as I put the two unlike magnetic poles together. Then watch the repulsion when I put the two like poles together. The magnetic force is greatest at the pole, but the magnetic field is all around the magnet. This diagram with lines of force shows you this.

    Electromagnetism is how electricity and magnetism work together. You can see this using a simple electromagnet made of a wire coil and an iron nail core connected to a battery. Hook it up, and you have a magnet. Unhook it, and the magnet is gone.

TAKE-HOME ACTIVITY

Assign the Take-Home Activity to students for additional practice with the target vocabulary words. The reproducible Take-Home Activity for Lesson 14 is on page 97 of the Teacher Guide.

TAKE HOME 14

magnetism   magnetic pole   magnetic field   electromagnetism
permanent magnet   attraction   lines of force   electromagnet
magnetize   repulsion

Use vocabulary words to complete the puzzle.

Magnetism

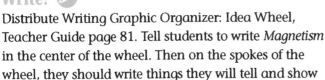

ACROSS

2 the push of like poles of magnets away from each other
5 the interaction of electricity and magnetism
7 the pull of unlike poles of magnets toward each other
8 the force produced by the motion of electrons within matter
9 lines that indicate the magnetic field, showing where force is strongest and weakest

DOWN

1 the region of force around a magnet
3 a magnet in which the particles stay lined up so the magnetism lasts
4 a device that develops magnetism when an electric current passes through it
6 a place on a magnet where the magnetic force is strongest
8 to turn an object into a magnet

 Tell someone in your family what you have learned about magnetism.

©Curriculum Associates, LLC *Passwords: Science Vocabulary, Physical Science, Lesson 14*   97

LESSON 15

Electric Power Production and Use

(Student Book pages 88–93)

TARGET VOCABULARY

ampere the unit of measure for flow rate, or amount of current

voltage the force available to move an electric current

volt the unit of measure for voltage

watt the unit of measure for power

power station a plant for producing electric power

turbine a group of curved blades that produce mechanical energy

generator a machine that produces electricity

transformer a device to change the voltage of a current

meter a tool to measure current used

fuse a safety device to break an overloaded circuit

COGNATES

Spanish-speaking students may find a discussion of the similarities and differences between English and Spanish cognates helpful.

English	Spanish
ampere	amperio
voltage	voltaje
volt	voltio
watt	vatio
station	estación
turbine	turbina
generator	generador
transformer	transformador
fuse	fusible

VOCABULARY STRATEGY: Suffixes

Have students find the target vocabulary word that uses the suffix *-age* (voltage) and the target vocabulary word that is the root word *(volt)*. Ask volunteers how the two nouns are related. *(Voltage is the force to move a current, which is measured using the volt.)* Tell students that *ampere* and *watt* each

have a related noun ending in *-age*. Have students guess these words or find them in a dictionary and explain the meaning of each word. *(Amperage is the amount of current, measured using the ampere; wattage is the amount of power, measured using the watt.)*

Lesson Summary Electric current is described using volts to measure voltage, amperes to measure flow rate, and watts to measure power. In a power station, a turbine produces mechanical energy from various energy sources, such as wind or the burning of fossil fuels. The turbine turns a coil of wire through a magnetic field in a generator to produce current. Transformers adjust the voltage for transport and then again for use. A meter records the current used by a consumer. Fuses or circuit breakers help prevent electrical fires.

BEFORE READING

Activate Prior Knowledge

Ask students to name sources of energy that are used to make electric power *(wind, moving water, tides, steam from the burning of fossil fuels, nuclear reactions, etc.)* and write these on the board. Show students pictures of some of these sources; for example, huge fields of wind generators, dams with hydroelectric power plants, coal-burning power plants, etc.

Introduce Target Vocabulary

Tell students they are about to read a selection about electric power production and use. Write the target vocabulary words on the board. Model the pronunciation of each word and have student volunteers repeat the word. Discuss the meaning of each word and, if necessary, write the definition next to the word.

Present Graphic Organizer

Provide each student with a copy of Vocabulary Graphic Organizer: Word Arrow, Teacher Guide page 79. Have students title the arrow *Electric Power Production and Use*. As they read the lesson, have them write target vocabulary words that refer to power production in the arrow from left to right, from producing to using the power. They should write the target vocabulary words that can describe electric currents in the space below the arrow.

Word and Definition Cards
for Lesson 15 are on pages 127 and 128
of the Teacher Guide.

Electric Power Production and Use

ampere	volt	power station	generator	meter
voltage	watt	turbine	transformer	fuse

You flip a switch, and a bulb lights up. You know that's because of electricity. How is electricity produced, and how does it get to you? Read this lesson to learn how.

Electric Power Production and Use

Measuring Electricity

Electricity is the flow of an electric current along a circuit to provide power. The amount of current is the number of electrons passing a given point in a circuit in one second. The unit used to measure the rate at which current flows is the **ampere**, or amp (A). An ampere is 6.25×10^{18} electrons per second.

Voltage is the amount of force available to move an electric current. The unit of measure for voltage is the **volt** (V).

A **watt** is a unit for measuring electrical power. To find the number of watts an electrical device uses, you multiply the current by the voltage. For a light bulb, a higher number of watts means a brighter light that uses more energy.

Voltage is like the pressure that pushes the water upward. Current is like the water.

Average Watts for Some Common Appliances	
Lamp	100
Fan	150
Computer	150
Television	200
Refrigerator	500
Toaster	1,100
Microwave	1,450
Dishwasher	2,000
Clothes dryer	5,000

Generating Electricity

Electric power is created in a plant called a **power station**. The first step is done with a turbine. A **turbine** is a group of curved blades mounted on a central rod, or shaft. Wind, moving water, or steam produced by burning fuel make the blades spin. As they rotate, the shaft turns too. The shaft then drives the **generator**, the machine that produces the electricity. The generator produces an electric current by using mechanical energy from the turbine to turn a coil of wire through a magnetic field. The magnetic field is the area of force around a magnet.

A Hydroelectric Power Station

Moving Electricity for Use

The current from a generator is adjusted before it is sent out to homes and businesses. A **transformer** is a device that changes the voltage of the current. Power companies use transformers to increase, or step up, the voltage produced. The result is less electricity being lost along the wires that carry it.

When the electricity reaches homes, transformers decrease, or step down, the voltage so that electrical appliances will operate correctly. The amount of electricity used inside a home is recorded on a **meter**. The power company uses the meter reading to bill the consumer.

An electric meter measures the amount of electricity used.

Electrical Safety

If too much current runs through a wire circuit, such as when too many appliances are connected, the wire can heat up and start a fire or shock someone. A **fuse** is a device that is used to break the circuit and stop the current. A fuse contains a thin wire that melts or breaks when the current gets too strong so that no more electricity will flow.

My Science Vocabulary

Go to page 98 to list other words you have learned about electric power production and use.

DURING READING

Read the selection aloud to students, stopping at the end of each paragraph or section. Review any words or concepts that students are having trouble with. Remind students that there is a glossary at the back of their book that contains all of the words that appear in boldfaced type in the lesson.

- Tell students that *volt*, *ampere*, and *watt* are all words that come from the names of scientists. *Volt* comes from Count Alessandro Volta, 1745–1827, an Italian pioneer in electricity; *ampere* is from Andre Marie Ampere, 1775–1836, the father of electrodynamics; *watt* is from James Watt, 1736–1819, a Scottish engineer and inventor.

- Have students define *power station* (*the place where electric power is made*). Then have them brainstorm other phrases that use the word *power* (*power boat, power drill, power house, power play,* etc.) Point out that power can mean (1) "the ability to act or perform," or (2) "the product created by that ability." Ask which meaning best applies to *power plant (meaning 2)*.

- Refer students to the diagram of power production on page 89 of the lesson. Have a volunteer read each label from left to right. After the label is read, have a student describe what is happening at that step in the process.

Have students read the selection again on their own.

AFTER READING

Review Graphic Organizers

Answer any questions students have about the reading selection. Then have students complete or review their graphic organizer and share it with the class.

Summarize

Have students work together to come up with either a written or an oral summary of the lesson. Encourage students to use the target vocabulary words as the basis of their summary. Have students share their summary with the class.

My Science Vocabulary

Encourage students to turn to My Science Vocabulary on page 98 of the student book and use the space provided to add other words about electric power production and use.

A. *Fill in the blanks with the correct vocabulary word.*

1. a device that breaks a circuit and stops the current
   f u s e

2. the unit of measure for voltage
   v o l t

3. a device that changes the voltage of a current
   t r a n s f o r m e r

4. a unit for measuring electrical power
   w a t t

5. a device that records the amount of electricity a home uses
   m e t e r

6. a group of curved blades on a shaft used to run a machine
   t u r b i n e

7. a machine that produces electricity
   g e n e r a t o r

8. the amount of force available to move an electric current
   v o l t a g e

9. the unit used to measure the flow rate of an electric current
   a m p e r e

10. a plant in which electric power is made
   p o w e r s t a t i o n

B. *Circle the word that makes sense in each sentence. Then write the word.*

1. Companies produce electric power in a plant called a (power station, transformer). _____ power station _____

2. A (fuse, meter) tells the power company how much electricity is used inside a home. _____ meter _____

3. Curved blades that can be turned by wind or water power, for example, make up a (generator, turbine). _____ turbine _____

4. The unit that measures the power of an electric current, found by multiplying voltage times current, is the (ampere, watt). _____ watt _____

5. To bring the current down to the correct voltage for home use, companies use a (transformer, fuse). _____ transformer _____

6. A machine that produces electricity is an electric (generator, transformer). _____ generator _____

7. The energy available to move a current is the (watt, voltage). _____ voltage _____

8. The unit called the (turbine, ampere) is used to measure flow rate of an electric current. _____ ampere _____

9. A device called a (watt, fuse) breaks an overloaded electrical circuit. _____ fuse _____

10. The unit of measure for voltage is the (fuse, volt). _____ volt _____

ROOT
The word **turbine** has its basis in the Latin root **turbia**, which means "a spinning thing or a whirlwind."

ACTIVITIES A–D

Encourage students to complete as many of the activities as possible. Remind students that they may refer to the Glossary at the back of their book as they complete the activities. Students may work independently, in small groups, or as a class. When students are done, discuss the answers for each activity.

Extensions

These extension ideas allow you to reuse or expand upon the activities. Share them with students who complete the activities before other students, or have students do them for additional practice with the target vocabulary words.

A Write complete sentences using each definition and its matching target vocabulary word.

B Choose five sentences and draw a diagram or picture to illustrate each one.

WORD ROOT

Ask students how the meaning "a spinning thing" relates to *turbine (a turbine has blades that spin)*. The prefix *turbo-* indicates *turbine*. Ask students to list words that use *turbo-* (*turbojet, turboprop, turbofan, turbosupercharger*). Encourage students to add these words to the prefix chart on page 100 of their book.

C Make four columns labeled: *1 Syllable, 2 Syllables, 3 Syllables, 4 Syllables*. Write the target vocabulary words in the correct column.

D For each pair of words, write a second sentence that uses the two words in the opposite order of your original sentence.

ampere   volt   power station   generator   meter
voltage   watt   turbine   transformer   fuse

C. *Choose the correct vocabulary word to complete each sentence.*

1. The voltage of a current can be measured using a unit called the ___volt___ .

2. When the blades of a ___turbine___ turn, the shaft rotates.

3. The thin wire inside a ___fuse___ melts or breaks when an electric current gets too strong.

4. The amount of electric current used by a consumer is measured by a ___meter___ .

5. For appliances to operate correctly, the ___voltage___ of the electrical current must be decreased.

6. To prevent energy from being lost along wires, a power station uses a ___transformer___ to increase, or step up, the voltage.

7. The flow rate of current is measured using a unit called the ___ampere___ .

8. The power of an electric current can be measured using a unit called the ___watt___ .

9. The building in which electricity is created is called a ___power station___ .

10. Using a coil of wire in a magnetic field, a ___generator___ makes electricity.

Electric Power Production and Use

---

ampere   volt   power station   generator   meter
voltage   watt   turbine   transformer   fuse

Students' answers will vary.

D. *Use each pair of words in a sentence.*

1. voltage, volt

The unit of measure for voltage, or the energy available to move current, is the volt.

2. ampere, watt
An ampere measures the flow rate of an electric current, and a watt measures its power.

3. fuse, meter
A meter records the amount of electricity being used within a home, and a fuse helps prevent electrical fires.

4. power station, transformer
Once it has been produced in a power station, electricity goes through a transformer to step up the voltage.

5. generator, turbine
The mechanical energy of a turbine turns a coil of wire inside a generator to produce electricity.

Write!
Write your response to the prompt on a separate sheet of paper. Use as many vocabulary words as you can in your writing.

You are an on-the-spot reporter following electricity from a power station to a home or business. Describe how electricity is created and how it changes.

Electric Power Production and Use

Write!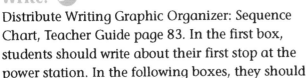

Distribute Writing Graphic Organizer: Sequence Chart, Teacher Guide page 83. In the first box, students should write about their first stop at the power station. In the following boxes, they should write in order what happens at each place that they visit along the route to a home or business.

Sample Answer

   I've gone to a power station, and I can see the turbine spinning. The shaft is moving the coil of wire in an electric generator. Electric current is flowing into a transformer where the voltage is increased and the current is decreased. So, as it moves along now, the current has more volts but fewer amperes.

   Now the current moves through another transformer that lowers voltage so it won't blow a fuse. A meter records the electricity going into a house. The current I'm watching just turned on a 100-watt bulb!

TAKE-HOME ACTIVITY

Assign the Take-Home Activity to students for additional practice with the target vocabulary words. The reproducible Take-Home Activity for Lesson 15 is on page 98 of the Teacher Guide.

Electric Power Production and Use

TAKE HOME 15

ampere   volt   power station   generator   meter
voltage   watt   turbine   transformer   fuse

Use vocabulary words to complete the puzzle.

Electric Power Production and Use

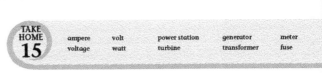
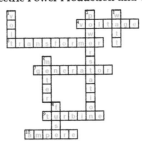

ACROSS

4 the force available to move a current

5 a device that changes the voltage of the current

7 a machine that produces electric current

9 a group of curved blades mounted on a central rod

10 the unit to measure flow rate, or the amount of current

DOWN

1 the unit of measure for voltage

2 a plant for producing electric power

3 a unit for measuring electrical power

6 the gauge that records the electric current being used

8 a device used to break a circuit to stop the flow of electricity and prevent a fire

Tell someone in your family what you have learned about electric power production and use.

Vocabulary Graphic Organizer: Word Web

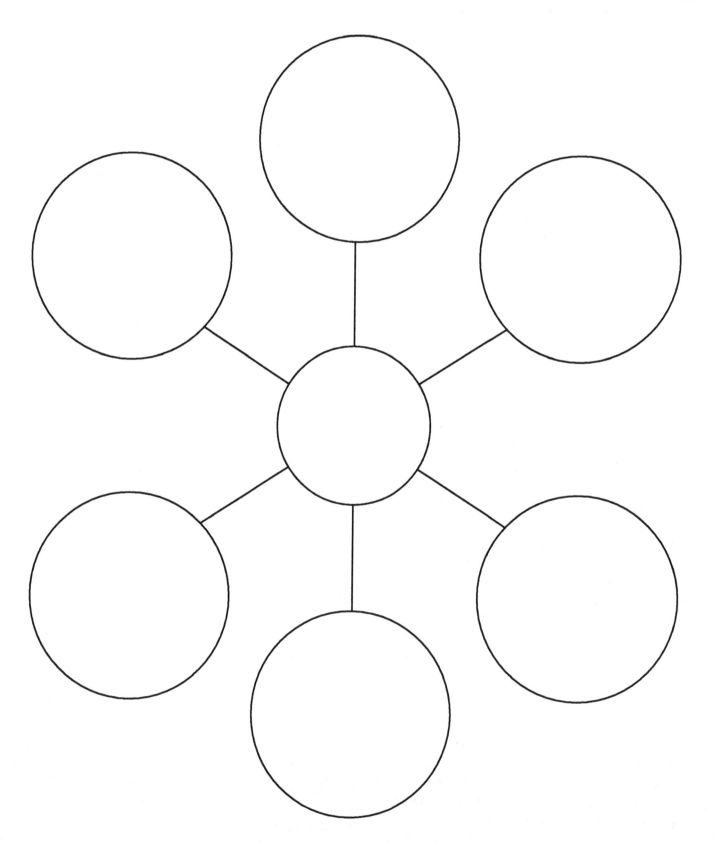

Name _____ Date _____

Vocabulary Graphic Organizer: Word Chart

Word	
Definition	
Examples	
Sentence	

Picture, Diagram, or Equation

Vocabulary Graphic Organizer: Four Square

Illustrate the word.	Use the word in a sentence.

Word

Definition	Word parts (root, prefix, suffix)

Vocabulary Graphic Organizer: Word Arrow

_____

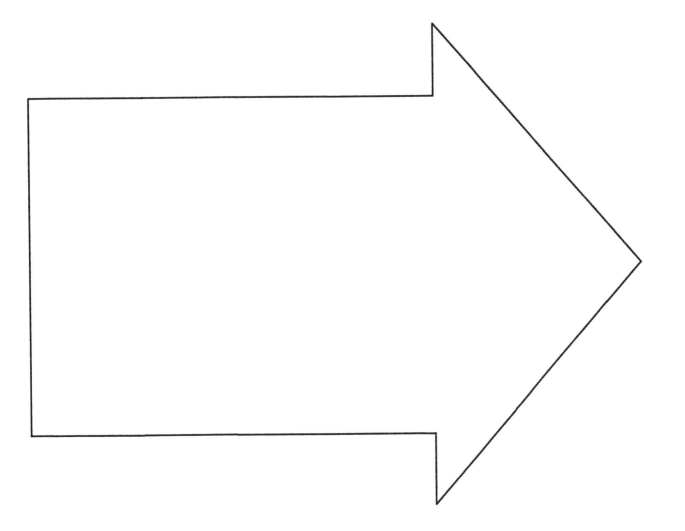

Name _____ Date _____

Writing Graphic Organizer: Main Idea and Details Chart

Main Idea	Details
1. _____ _____ _____ _____ _____ _____ _____	_____ _____ _____ _____ _____ _____ _____
2. _____ _____ _____ _____ _____ _____ _____	_____ _____ _____ _____ _____ _____ _____
3. _____ _____ _____ _____ _____ _____ _____	_____ _____ _____ _____ _____ _____ _____

Writing Graphic Organizer: Idea Wheel

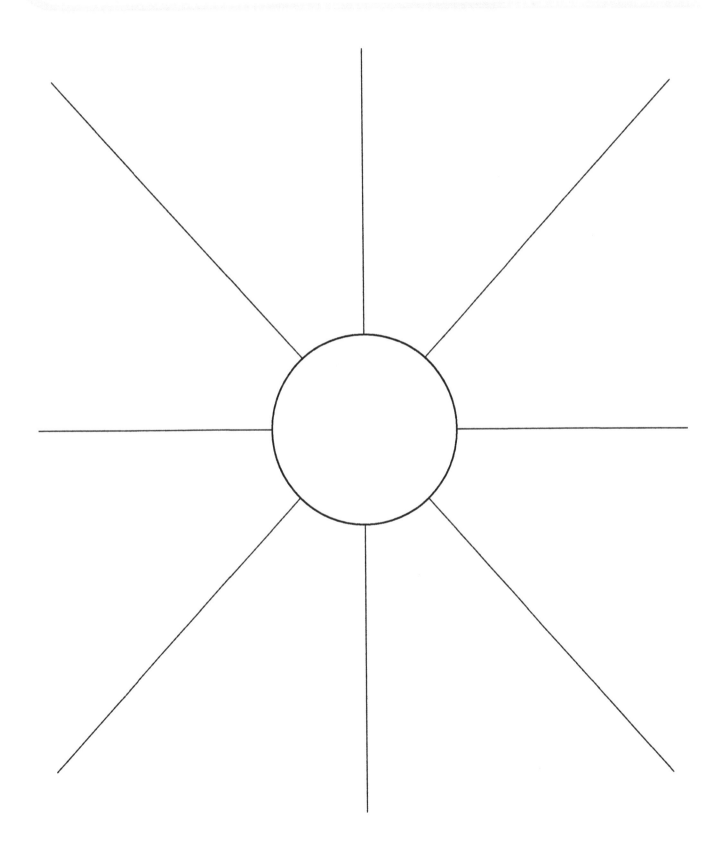

Writing Graphic Organizer: Narrative Map

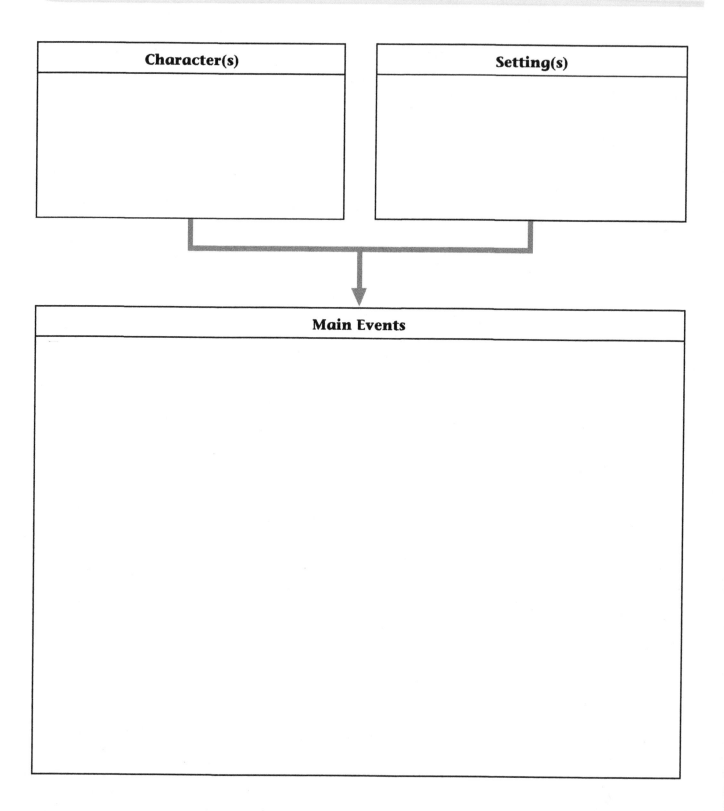

Character(s)	Setting(s)

Main Events

©Curriculum Associates, LLC *Passwords: Science Vocabulary, Physical Science*

Name _____ Date _____

Writing Graphic Organizer: Sequence Chart

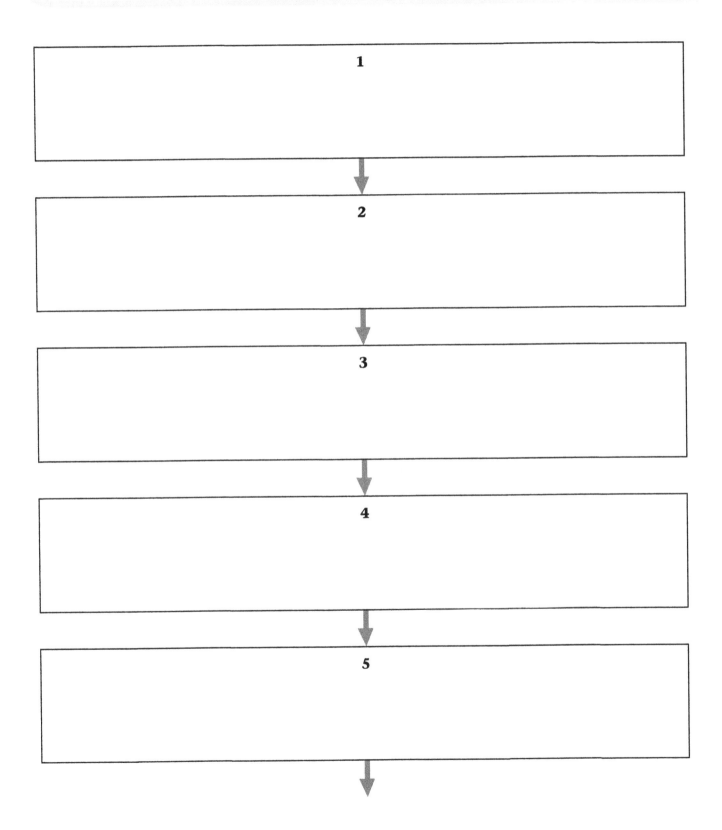

mass   density   displacement   melting point   boiling point
volume   buoyant force   physical change   freezing point   chemical change

Use vocabulary words to complete the puzzle.

Properties and Changes of Matter

ACROSS

4 a change creating new substances

6 the volume of fluid pushed aside by an object placed in the fluid

7 the temperature at which a liquid changes to a gas

8 the amount of matter

9 how tightly packed matter is

DOWN

1 how much space matter takes up

2 the temperature at which a liquid changes to a solid

3 a change in the size, shape, or state of matter

5 the temperature at which a solid changes to a liquid

7 the upward force of a fluid

Tell someone in your family what you have learned about properties and changes of matter.

element   atom   nucleus   positive charge   electron

compound   molecule   proton   neutron   negative charge

Use vocabulary words to complete the puzzle.

The Structure of Matter

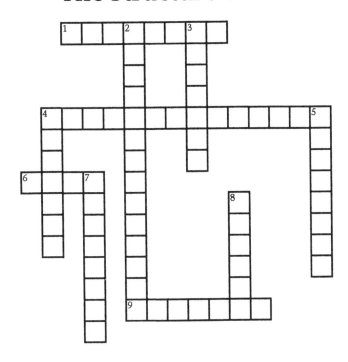

ACROSS

1   a substance made up of two or more elements

4   an electric charge of less than zero

6   the smallest unit of an element that still has the properties of that element

9   a substance that cannot be broken down into simpler substances by chemical change

DOWN

2   an electric charge greater than zero

3   the part of the atom that has the greatest amount of matter

4   an atomic particle that has no charge

5   an atomic particle that orbits the nucleus

7   the smallest unit of a compound that still has the compound's properties

8   an atomic particle with a positive charge

Tell someone in your family what you have learned about the structure of matter.

periodic table   atomic number   chemical property   nonmetal   noble gas

chemical symbol   atomic mass   hydrogen   metalloid   helium

Use vocabulary words to complete the puzzle.

The Periodic Table of Elements

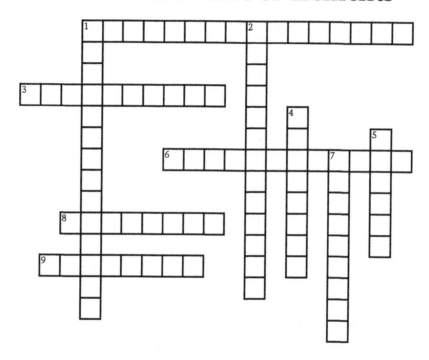

ACROSS

1 the way an element acts with other elements

3 the amount of matter of an atom

6 the number of protons in the nucleus of an atom

8 the gas with an atomic number of 1

9 a type of gas that does not normally combine with other elements

DOWN

1 the one- or two-letter abbreviation for an element

2 a chart that groups elements by properties

4 an element with no metallic properties

5 the noble gas with an atomic number of 2

7 an element with some properties of metals and some of nonmetals

Tell someone in your family what you have learned about the periodic table of elements.

©Curriculum Associates, LLC *Passwords: Science Vocabulary, Physical Science, Lesson 3*

chemistry   reactant   chemical equation   solvent
chemical bond product   solution   solute
chemical reaction chemical formula

Use vocabulary words to complete the puzzle.

The Science of Chemistry

ACROSS

1 a change in which chemical bonds are broken or made

5 the study of matter and how it changes

7 the substance that dissolves in the solvent

8 the raw material of a chemical reaction

9 a mixture that is the same throughout

DOWN

1 an expression that uses chemical formulas and symbols to show the reactants and products of a chemical reaction

2 the symbols and numbers that show what a compound is made of

3 the force that joins atoms in a compound

4 the substance that forms as a result of a chemical reaction

6 the substance that dissolves another substance in a solution

Tell someone in your family what you have learned about the science of chemistry.

acid   soluble   alkaline   neutral   litmus paper
ion   base   pH   indicator   neutralize

Use vocabulary words to complete the puzzle.

Acids and Bases

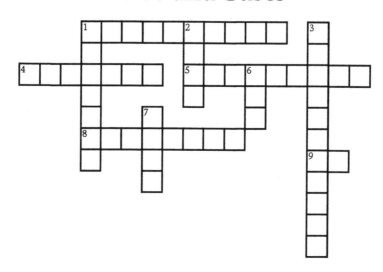

ACROSS

1 to make neutral

4 able to be dissolved

5 a substance that changes color to show whether a solution is an acid or a base

8 having the characteristics of a base

9 a measure on a scale from 0 to 14 of how acidic or alkaline a solution is

DOWN

1 neither acid nor alkaline

2 a substance that produces hydrogen ions in water

3 a specially treated paper that is used as an indicator

6 an atom or atoms with an electric charge

7 a substance that produces hydroxide ions when it dissolves in water

Tell someone in your family what you have learned about acids and bases.

TAKE HOME 6

| inertia | momentum | acceleration | net force | action force |
| balanced forces | velocity | unbalanced forces | friction | reaction force |

Use vocabulary words to complete the puzzle.

Motion and Forces

ACROSS

3 forces that cause a change in velocity

5 a measure of an object's motion

7 the tendency of an object to resist changes in motion

8 a force that opposes motion when two objects are in contact

9 a change in velocity

10 the difference in strength and direction of all the forces acting on an object

DOWN

1 the forces acting on an object when it is at rest

2 the force opposing the action force

4 the force acting on an object

6 the speed and direction of an object

Tell someone in your family what you have learned about motion and forces.

Use vocabulary words to complete the puzzle.

Simple Machines

ACROSS

5 the number of times a machine multiplies the effort force

7 a measure of how much work a machine does compared to the effort used

9 a simple machine with a bar that moves around a fixed point

10 an inclined plane that moves

DOWN

1 a wheel with a rope or chain around it that changes the direction of the force

2 the force that opposes the effort force

3 a simple machine made of a wheel with a rod in the center

4 a ramp

6 the force used to move an object

8 an inclined plane wrapped in a spiral around a cylinder

Tell someone in your family what you have learned about simple machines.

kinetic energy   electrical energy   nuclear energy   energy transformation

potential energy   thermal energy   radiant energy   solar energy

mechanical energy   chemical energy

Use vocabulary words to complete the puzzle.

Forms of Energy

ACROSS

5 the change of one form of energy to another

8 energy released from a chemical reaction

9 energy that moves in waves

10 heat energy

DOWN

1 radiant energy from the sun

2 energy produced by the movement of electrons

3 energy produced by the motion of an object

4 the total amount of potential and kinetic energy an object has

6 energy given off when the nucleus of an atom breaks apart

7 stored energy

Tell someone in your family what you have learned about forms of energy.

wave   longitudinal wave   trough   amplitude   reflection

transverse wave   crest   wavelength   frequency   refraction

Use vocabulary words to complete the puzzle.

The Properties of Waves

ACROSS

1 the distance between the crest of one wave and the crest of the next wave

4 a measure of how much a wave moves up and down

5 the high point of a wave

8 the number of waves that pass a certain point in a given time

9 the lowest point of a wave

DOWN

1 a disturbance that transfers energy

2 a wave that moves matter backward and forward in the same direction the wave is moving

3 a wave that moves matter up and down at a right angle to the direction the wave is moving

6 the bouncing back of a wave

7 the bending of a wave caused by a change of speed as the wave moves from one type of matter to another

Tell someone in your family what you have learned about the properties of waves.

heat transfer   convection   expansion   Fahrenheit scale   Kelvin scale

conduction   radiation   contraction   Celsius scale   calorie

Use vocabulary words to complete the puzzle.

Heat

ACROSS

2 the transfer of heat that happens when molecules move

3 the scale on which 0 means the kinetic energy is zero

6 the scale with 32° as the freezing point and 212° as the boiling point of water

8 the heat transfer by energy waves

9 an increase in volume

DOWN

1 a decrease in volume

2 the heat transfer that occurs when molecules have direct contact

4 the energy needed to raise 1 gram of water 1° Celsius

5 the scale with 0° as the freezing point and 100° as the boiling point of water

7 the moving of heat from a cooler substance to a warmer one

Tell someone in your family what you have learned about heat.

vibration	medium	decibel	hertz	echo
vacuum	volume	pitch	ultrasound	sonar

Use vocabulary words to complete the puzzle.

Sound Energy

ACROSS

2 an up-and-down or back-and-forth movement

4 sound above the normal human range of hearing

5 any matter that sound travels through

7 the unit that measures the pitch, or frequency, of sound

8 how high or low sound is

9 the reflection of sound waves

DOWN

1 the use of ultrasonic sound waves and echoes for underwater exploration

2 a place empty of matter

3 loudness of sound

6 the unit of measure for volume

Tell someone in your family what you have learned about sound energy.

electromagnetic spectrum   infrared radiation   translucent   convex lens
visible light   ultraviolet light   transparent   concave lens
prism   opaque

Use vocabulary words to complete the puzzle.

Light Energy

ACROSS

2   the total range of radiant energy

4   letting almost all light pass through

5   letting some light pass through

6   a lens that is thinner at the center than at the edges

7   the part of the electromagnetic spectrum that people can see

9   radiant energy with a longer wavelength than visible light

DOWN

1   radiant energy with a shorter wavelength than visible light

3   a lens that is thicker at the center than at the edges

8   a triangle-shaped piece of glass that bends light

10   blocking light

Tell someone in your family what you have learned about light energy.

conductor   resistance   electric circuit   series circuit   direct current
insulator   ohm   battery   parallel circuit   alternating current

Use vocabulary words to complete the puzzle.

Electricity

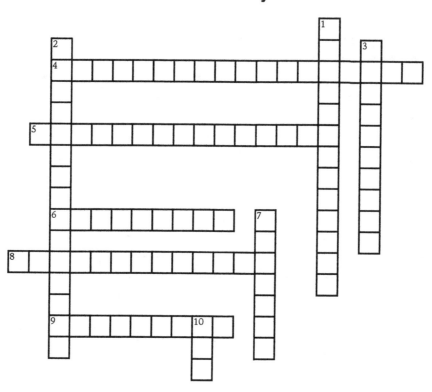

ACROSS

4 current that rapidly switches direction

5 the complete path electricity follows

6 a material that lets electrons pass through it easily

8 a circuit with only one path for electricity to follow

9 material that does not let electricity pass through it easily

DOWN

1 electric current that flows in only one direction

2 a circuit with two or more paths for electricity to follow

3 how much a substance opposes the flow of electrons

7 a source of electricity from chemical reactions

10 the unit of measure for resistance

Tell someone in your family what you have learned about electricity.

magnetism   magnetic pole   magnetic field   electromagnetism

permanent magnet   attraction   lines of force   electromagnet

magnetize   repulsion

Use vocabulary words to complete the puzzle.

Magnetism

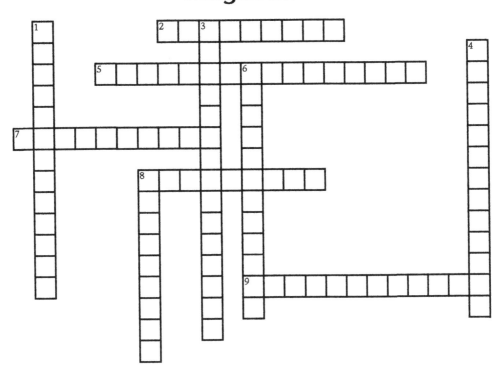

ACROSS

2 the push of like poles of magnets away from each other

5 the interaction of electricity and magnetism

7 the pull of unlike poles of magnets toward each other

8 the force produced by the motion of electrons within matter

9 lines that indicate the magnetic field, showing where force is strongest and weakest

DOWN

1 the region of force around a magnet

3 a magnet in which the particles stay lined up so the magnetism lasts

4 a device that develops magnetism when an electric current passes through it

6 a place on a magnet where the magnetic force is strongest

8 to turn an object into a magnet

Tell someone in your family what you have learned about magnetism.

ampere   volt   power station   generator   meter

voltage   watt   turbine   transformer   fuse

Use vocabulary words to complete the puzzle.

Electric Power Production and Use

ACROSS

4   the force available to move a current

5   a device that changes the voltage of the current

7   a machine that produces electric current

9   a group of curved blades mounted on a central rod

10   the unit to measure flow rate, or the amount of current

DOWN

1   the unit of measure for voltage

2   a plant for producing electric power

3   a unit for measuring electrical power

6   the gauge that records the electric current being used

8   a device used to break a circuit to stop the flow of electricity and prevent a fire

Tell someone in your family what you have learned about electric power production and use.

mass	physical change
volume	melting point
density	freezing point
buoyant force	boiling point
displacement	chemical change

a change in the size, shape, or state of matter, with no new matter being formed

the amount of matter

the temperature at which a solid changes to a liquid

the amount of space that matter takes up

the temperature at which a liquid changes to a solid

the amount of matter packed into a certain volume

the temperature at which a liquid changes to a gas

the upward force applied by a fluid on an object placed in the fluid

a change in matter that creates one or more new substances

the volume of fluid pushed aside by an object placed in the fluid

element	proton
compound	positive charge
atom	neutron
molecule	electron
nucleus	negative charge

a particle in the nucleus of an atom with a positive electric charge

a substance that cannot be broken down into simpler substances by chemical change

an electric charge greater than zero

a substance made up of two or more elements

a particle in the nucleus of an atom with no electric charge

the smallest unit of an element that still has the properties of that element

a particle in an atom that orbits the nucleus in a sort of cloud and has a negative charge

the smallest unit of a compound that still has the properties of that compound

an electric charge less than zero

the center of an atom, containing most of the atom's mass and one or more protons and neutrons

periodic table	hydrogen
chemical symbol	nonmetal
atomic number	metalloid
atomic mass	noble gas
chemical property	helium

a gas with an atomic number and atomic mass of 1

a table that organizes the elements into rows and columns by their properties

an element that has no metallic properties

a one- or two-letter abbreviation that stands for the name of an element

an element that has some properties of metals and some properties of nonmetals

the number of protons in the nucleus of an atom

a gas that is a nonmetal and does not normally combine with other elements

the mass of an atom, which is almost equal to the total number of protons and neutrons in the atom

a noble gas with an atomic number of 2

the way in which an element acts with other elements

chemistry	chemical formula
chemical bond	chemical equation
chemical reaction	solution
reactant	solvent
product	solute

a set of symbols and numbers that shows the elements in a compound and the number of atoms of each element

the science of matter and how it changes

an expression that uses chemical formulas and symbols to show the reactants and products of a chemical reaction

a force of attraction that holds together the atoms in a compound

a mixture in which the particles of each substance are mixed evenly

a change in which chemical bonds are broken or made, forming new substances

a substance that dissolves another substance to form a solution

one of the raw materials of a chemical reaction

a substance that is dissolved in another substance, forming a solution

one of the end results of a chemical reaction

 Passwords: Science Vocabulary, Physical Science, Lesson 4—Word Cards

ion	pH
acid	neutral
soluble	indicator
base	litmus paper
alkaline	neutralize

a measure on a scale from 0 to 14 of how acidic or alkaline a solution is

an atom or group of atoms with an electric charge.

neither an acid nor a base

a substance that forms hydrogen ions when it is dissolved in water

a substance that changes color to indicate whether a solution is an acid or a base

able to be dissolved

an indicator made of treated paper that shows whether a solution is an acid or a base

a substance that produces hydroxide ions when it is dissolved in water

to change acids and bases by chemical reaction into neutral products

having the properties of a base

inertia	unbalanced forces
balanced forces	net force
momentum	action force
velocity	friction
acceleration	reaction force

the forces acting on an object that cause a change in velocity

the tendency of an object at rest to stay at rest and an object in motion to stay in motion in the same direction

the total difference in strength and direction of all the forces acting on an object

the forces acting on an object when it is at rest or moving at a constant speed in a constant direction

the force acting on an object

the measure of an object's motion

a force that opposes motion when two objects are in contact

a measure of an object's speed and direction of motion

a force pushing equally hard in the opposite direction of an action force

the change in an object's velocity

effort force	wedge
resistance force	screw
mechanical advantage	lever
efficiency	wheel and axle
inclined plane	pulley

a simple machine consisting of an inclined plane that moves

the force used to move an object

a simple machine that is an inclined plane wrapped in a spiral around a cylinder

the force that opposes the effort force

a simple machine made of a bar that moves on a fixed point

the number of times a machine multiplies the effort force

a simple machine that is a wheel attached to a rod, or axle

the measure of how much work a machine does compared to the effort, or energy, used

a simple machine that consists of a wheel with a rope or chain around it

a simple machine that is a ramp

kinetic energy	chemical energy
potential energy	nuclear energy
mechanical energy	radiant energy
electrical energy	energy transformation
thermal energy	solar energy

energy stored in the bonds that hold molecules together and released when the bonds break during a chemical reaction

the energy of motion

energy released when the nucleus of an atom breaks apart or fuses with the nucleus of another atom

energy that is not being used, or stored energy

energy that moves in waves through matter

the total amount of potential and kinetic energy that an object has

the changing of energy from one form to another

energy produced by moving electrons

energy from the sun

energy produced by the movement of molecules, or heat

wave	wavelength
transverse wave	amplitude
longitudinal wave	frequency
crest	reflection
trough	refraction

the distance between the crest on one wave and the crest on the next wave

a disturbance that transfers energy through matter or through space

the distance between a crest or trough and the horizontal center line of a wave

a wave that moves matter up and down, at a right angle to the direction the wave is moving

the number of waves that pass a certain point in a given amount of time

a wave that moves matter backward and forward, in the same direction the wave is moving

the bouncing back of a wave that hits a surface

the high point of a transverse wave

the bending of a wave caused by a change of speed as the wave moves from one type of matter to another

the low point of a transverse wave

 Passwords: Science Vocabulary, Physical Science, Lesson 9—Word Cards

expansion	radiation
contraction	Fahrenheit scale
heat transfer	Celsius scale
conduction	Kelvin scale
convection	calorie

the transfer of heat in the form of energy waves

an increase in the volume of matter caused by heating

a temperature scale on which water freezes at 32° and water boils at 212°

a decrease in the volume of matter caused by cooling

a temperature scale on which water freezes at 0° and water boils at 100°

the movement of heat energy from matter with a higher temperature to matter with a lower temperature

a temperature scale based on a unit called the kelvin (K). On this scale, water freezes at 273 K and boils at 373 K.

the transfer of heat that happens when molecules of matter have direct contact

a measure of heat energy equal to the amount of energy needed to raise the temperature of one gram of water one degree Celsius

the transfer of heat that happens when molecules of matter move from one place to another

 Passwords: Science Vocabulary, Physical Science, Lesson 10—Word Cards

vibration	pitch
vacuum	hertz
medium	ultrasound
volume	echo
decibel	sonar

how high or low sound is, based on the speed, or frequency, of the sound waves

the up-and-down or back-and-forth movement of an object that produces sound

the unit of measure for pitch, based on the frequency of the sound waves

a place empty of matter

sound that is above the range of human hearing

the matter through which sound waves travel. Sound can travel through a solid, liquid, or gas.

the reflection of sound waves

how loud a sound is, which depends on the amplitude, or amount of energy in the sound waves

the system of using ultrasound and its echoes for underwater exploration

the unit of measure used to describe volume

electromagnetic spectrum	opaque
visible light	translucent
prism	transparent
infrared radiation	convex lens
ultraviolet light	concave lens

blocking light from passing through

the total range of radiant energy that includes such forms as radio waves, microwaves, infrared radiation, visible light, ultraviolet light, and x-rays

allowing some light to pass through and scattering some light

the range of electromagnetic waves that people are able to see

allowing almost all the light striking the surface to pass through

a triangle-shaped piece of glass that bends white light into its colors

a lens that is thicker at the center than at the edges

radiant energy in the invisible spectrum that has a longer wavelength and slower frequency than visible light

a lens that is thinner at the center than at the edges

radiant energy in the invisible spectrum that has a shorter wavelength and faster frequency than visible light

conductor	battery
insulator	series circuit
resistance	parallel circuit
ohm	direct current
electric circuit	alternating current

a source of electricity from chemical reactions

a material that lets electrons pass through it easily

a circuit with only one path for electricity to follow

a material that does not let electricity pass through it easily

a circuit with two or more paths for electricity to follow

how much a substance opposes the flow of electrons

electric current that is produced in a battery and flows in only one direction

the unit of measure for resistance

electric current that switches direction rapidly

a complete path from negative to positive along which electric charges, or electricity, can flow

 Passwords: Science Vocabulary, Physical Science, Lesson 13—Word Cards

magnetism

magnetic field

permanent magnet

lines of force

magnetic pole

electromagnetism

attraction

electromagnet

repulsion

magnetize

the region of force around a magnet

the force produced by the motion of electrons within matter

lines that indicate the magnetic field, showing where force is strongest and weakest

a magnet in which the particles stay lined up so the magnetism lasts

the interaction of electricity and magnetism

a place on a magnet where the magnetic force is the strongest

a device that develops magnetism when an electric current passes through it

the pull of unlike poles of magnets toward each other

to turn an object into a magnet

the push of like poles of magnets away from each other

©Curriculum Associates, LLC *Passwords: Science Vocabulary, Physical Science, Lesson 14—Word Cards*

voltage	turbine
volt	generator
ampere	transformer
watt	meter
power station	fuse

a group of curved blades that turn a shaft, which uses mechanical energy to run machines

the amount of force available to move an electric current

a machine that produces electricity by using a coil of wire moving through a magnetic field

the unit of measure for voltage

a device that adjusts the voltage and current of electricity for travel along wires and for home use

the unit of measure for the amount, or flow rate, of electric current

the gauge that measures the electric current used in a home so that the electric company can bill the consumer

a unit for measuring electrical power, found by multiplying voltage (volts) times current (amperes)

a device that breaks a circuit to stop the flow of electricity and prevent a fire

a plant where electricity is produced